Instructor's Manual

for

Kalat's

Biological Psychology

Eighth Edition

Cynthia Crawford

California State University at San Bernadino

James W. Kalat

North Carolina State University

 THOMSON

WADSWORTH

Australia • Canada • Mexico • Singapore • Spain • United Kingdom • United States

Printed in the United States of America
1 2 3 4 5 6 7   07 06 05 04 03

Printer: WestGroup

0-534-58820-4

For more information about our products, contact us at:
Thomson Learning Academic Resource Center
1-800-423-0563

For permission to use material from this text, contact us by:
Phone: 1-800-730-2214
Fax: 1-800-731-2215
Web: http://www.thomsonrights.com

Wadsworth/Thomson Learning
10 Davis Drive
Belmont, CA 94002-3098
USA

Asia
Thomson Learning
5 Shenton Way #01-01
UIC Building
Singapore 068808

Australia/New Zealand
Thomson Learning
102 Dodds Street
Southbank, Victoria 3006
Australia

Canada
Nelson
1120 Birchmount Road
Toronto, Ontario M1K 5G4
Canada

Europe/Middle East/South Africa
Thomson Learning
High Holborn House
50/51 Bedford Row
London WC1R 4LR
United Kingdom

Latin America
Thomson Learning
Seneca, 53
Colonia Polanco
11560 Mexico D.F.
Mexico

Spain/Portugal
Paraninfo
Calle/Magallanes, 25
28015 Madrid, Spain

TABLE OF CONTENTS

PREFACE

This instructor's manual has been developed to complement the eighth edition of James Kalat's *Biological Psychology* text. The manual contains chapter outlines, class activities and demonstrations including activities from internet sites and the Exploring Psychology CD-ROM, critical thinking exercises, and a catalog of multimedia and on-line resources. Dr. Kalat's answers to "thought questions" are also provided at the end of each chapter. The goal of the instructor's manual is to enhance the classroom experience of the student by providing practical direction and helpful information to the instructor. A brief description of each section is given below:

Chapter Outlines: Includes concise overviews of each chapter. These chapter overviews can be used as a bases for developing lecture notes.

Class Activities and Demonstrations: The activities and demonstrations are included to enhance student understanding of concepts critical to biological psychology and to facilitate the active learning process. Many of the activities are from the previous instructor's manual written by Ronald Ruiz (Riverside Community College). This section also includes activities from selected web sites and from the Exploring Biological Psychology CD-ROM.

Multimedia Resources: This section lists videotape suggestions from the CNN® Today Video and other sources for each chapter and available instructional aides from the Exploring Biological Psychology CD-ROM.

On-Line Resources: The on-line resources include the Biopsychology website, where students can access on-line quizzes for each chapter. This section also includes suggested websites for each chapter and provides students with keywords for the InfoTrac site that can be used for papers or in-class discussions.

Critical Thinking Exercises: These exercises are included to enhance critical thinking skills as they require students to use the concepts learned in the chapter and apply them to "real life" issues. They can be used for both class discussions or as exam questions.

CHAPTER 1 *The Major Issues*

CHAPTER OUTLINE	IDEAS FOR INSTRUCTION	PRINT RESOURCES	MEDIA & INTERNET RESOURCES
The Mind-Brain Relationship (Module 1.1) • Biological Explanations of Behavior • The Brain and Conscious Experience	Critical Thinking Exercise The Amazing Tale of Phineas Gage	Study Guide Chapter 1 Test Bank Chapter 1 includes approximately 200 multiple-choice items, 30 true/false items, and several essay questions. Also available in ExamView® electronic format.	Multimedia Manager Create a media lecture for Chapter 1 WebTutor™ Advantage Chapter 1 lecture notes, discussion threads, and quizzes on WebCT or Blackboard Web site For online quizzes, Web links, and more on Chapter 1, go to: http://psychology.wadsworth.com/book/kalatbiopsych8e/ InfoTrac® College Edition *Keywords:* biofeedback, consciousness (subdivision-research) Videos *Films for the Humanities and Sciences:* "How the Human Mind Works: Patricia Smith Churchland" (30 min) *Insight Media:* "Is Mind Distinct from Body" (30 min) Exploring Biological Psychology CD-ROM "Selection and Random Drift" "Critical Thinking" "Chapter Quiz"
The Genetics of Behavior (Module 1.2) • The Evolution of Behavior	Classroom Activity Evolution—A Historical Perspective Critical Thinking Exercise Evolution vs. Technology		InfoTrac® College Edition *Keywords:* personality and genes, sociobiology Video *Film Ideas:* "Genetics and Heredity: The Blue Print of Life" (27 min) Exploring Biological Psychology CD-ROM "Offspring of Parents Homozygous and Heterozygous for Brown Eyes" "RNA, DNA, and Protein"
The Use of Animals in Research (Module 1.3) • Reasons for Animal Research • The Ethical Debate	Classroom Activity Animal Rights vs. Animal Research Exercise		InfoTrac® College Edition *Keyword:* animal rights Videos *Foundation for Biomedical Research:* "Hope" (17 min) *Southwest Association for Education in Biomedical Research:* "Partners in Research" (13 min)
Prospects for Further Study (Module 1.4)			

CHAPTER 2 *Nerve Cells and Nerve Impulses*

CHAPTER OUTLINE	IDEAS FOR INSTRUCTION	PRINT RESOURCES	MEDIA & INTERNET RESOURCES
Cells of the Nervous System (Module 2.1) <ul><li>Anatomy of Neurons and Glia</li><li>Blood-Brain Barrier</li><li>Nourishment of Vertebrate Neurons</li></ul>	**Classroom Activity** Neuron slide show	**Study Guide** Chapter 2 **Test Bank** Chapter 2 includes approximately 200 multiple-choice items, 30 true/false items, and several essay questions. Also available in ExamView® electronic format.	**Multimedia Manager** Create a media lecture for Chapter 2 **WebTutor™ Advantage** Chapter 2 lecture notes, discussion threads, and quizzes on WebCT or Blackboard **Web site** For online quizzes, Web links, and more on Chapter 2, go to: http://psychology.wadsworth.com/book /kalatbiopsych8e/ **InfoTrac® College Edition** *Keywords:* blood-brain barrier, neurons (subdivision-growth) **Video** *Annenberg/CPB:* "The Behaving Brain" (30 min) **Exploring Biological Psychology CD-ROM** "The Parts of a Neuron" "Virtual Reality Neuron" "Neuron Puzzle" "Critical Thinking" "Chapter Quiz"
Nerve Impulse (Module 2.2) <ul><li>Resting Potential</li><li>Action Potential</li><li>Propagation of the Action Potential</li><li>Myelin Sheath and Saltatory Conduction</li><li>Local Neurons</li></ul>	**Classroom Activities** The Concentration Gradient Action Potential **Critical Thinking Exercises** Appreciating Myelin Cocaine		**InfoTrac® College Edition** *Keywords:* demyelination, epilepsy **Video** *Insight Media:* "The Nerve Impulse Conduction" (29 min) **Exploring Biological Psychology CD-ROM** "Resting Potential" "Action Potential" "Action Potential: Na⁺ Ions" "The Graphic Brain" "Neurons in Action"

CHAPTER 3 *Communication at Synapses*

CHAPTER OUTLINE	IDEAS FOR INSTRUCTION	PRINT RESOURCES	MEDIA & INTERNET RESOURCES
The Concept of the Synapse (Module 3.1) • The Properties of Synapses • Temporal and Spatial Summation • Relationship Among EPSP, IPSP, and Action Potential	**Classroom Activity** Reaction Time and Neural Circuitry **Critical Thinking Exercise** Electrical Synaptic Transmission	**Study Guide** Chapter 3 **Test Bank** Chapter 3 includes approximately 200 multiple-choice items, 30 true/false items, and several essay questions. Also available in ExamView® electronic format.	**Multimedia Manager** Create a media lecture for Chapter 3 **WebTutor™ Advantage** Chapter 3 lecture notes, discussion threads, and quizzes on WebCT or Blackboard **Web site** For online quizzes, Web links, and more on Chapter 3, go to: http://psychology.wadsworth.com/book /kalatbiopsych8e/ **InfoTrac® College Edition** *Keyword:* reaction time **Video** *Films for the Humanities and Sciences:* "The Electric Ape" (58 min) **Exploring Biological Psychology CD-ROM** "Postsynaptic Potentials" "Critical Thinking" "Chapter Quiz"
Chemical Events at the Synapse (Module 3.2) • The Discovery That Most Synaptic Transmission Is Chemical • The Sequence of Chemical Events at a Synapse • Types of Transmitters • Synthesis of Transmitters • Transport of Transmitters • Release and Diffusion of Transmitters • Activation of Receptors of the Postsynaptic Cell • Metabotropic Effects and Second Messenger Systems • Inactivation and Reuptake of Neurotransmitters • How Drugs Affect Synapses • Synapses and Personality	**Critical Thinking Exercises** Tryptophan Bliss		**InfoTrac® College Edition** *Keyword:* nerve gas **Videos** *Foundation for Biomedical Research:* "Bubble, Bubble, Toil, and Trouble" (58 min) *Films for the Humanities and Sciences:* "The Brain" (23 min) **Exploring Biological Psychology CD-ROM** "Release of Neurotransmitter" "Cholinergic" "Release of Ach" "AChE Inactivates ACh"

CHAPTER 4 *Anatomy of the Nervous System*

CHAPTER OUTLINE	IDEAS FOR INSTRUCTION	PRINT RESOURCES	MEDIA & INTERNET RESOURCES
Research Methods (Module 4.1) <ul><li>Effects of Brain Damage</li><li>Effects of Brain Stimulation</li><li>Recording Brain Activity</li><li>Correlating Brain Activity with Behavior</li></ul>	**Classroom Activity** Mapping the Motor Cortex **Critical Thinking Exercise** Measuring Brain Activity	**Study Guide** Chapter 4 **Test Bank** Chapter 4 includes approximately 200 multiple-choice items, 30 true/false items, and several essay questions. Also available in ExamView® electronic format.	**Multimedia Manager** Create a media lecture for Chapter 4 **WebTutor™ Advantage** Chapter 4 lecture notes, discussion threads, and quizzes on WebCT or Blackboard **Web site** For online quizzes, Web links, and more on Chapter 4, go to: http://psychology.wadsworth.com/book /kalatbiopsych8e/ **InfoTrac® College Edition** *Keyword:* brain imaging **CNN® Today Video** "New Brain Research," Volume 1, Segment 1 (2:41) **Video** *Films for the Humanities and Sciences:* "Brain and Nervous System: Your Information Superhighway" (31 min) **Exploring Biological Psychology CD-ROM** "Critical Thinking" "Chapter Quiz"
Structure of the Vertebrate Nervous System (Module 4.2) <ul><li>Nervous System Terminology</li><li>The Spinal Cord</li><li>The Autonomic Nervous System</li><li>The Hindbrain</li><li>The Midbrain</li><li>The Forebrain</li><li>The Ventricles</li></ul>	**Classroom Activities** Demonstration of External Sheep Brain Structures Demonstration on Human Brain Structure		**InfoTrac® College Edition** *Keywords:* lie detector, hydrocephalus **Video** *Films for the Humanities and Science:* "Anatomy of the Human Brain" (35 min) **Exploring Biological Psychology CD-ROM** "Virtual Reality Head Planes" "Planes Puzzle" "Virtual Reality Brain" "Left Hemisphere Function #1" "Sagittal Section: Right Hemisphere #1" "Sagittal Section: Right Hemisphere #2" "Sagittal Section: Right Hemisphere #3" "Brain Puzzle"
The Cerebral Cortex (Module 4.3) <ul><li>Organization of the Cerebral Cortex</li><li>The Occipital Lobe</li><li>The Parietal Lobe</li><li>The Temporal Lobe</li><li>The Frontal Lobe</li><li>How Do the Parts Work Together?</li></ul>	**Classroom Activity** Demonstration of the Sensory Homunculus **Critical Thinking Exercise** Working Memory vs. Short-Term Memory		**Video** *Annenberg/CPB:* "The Frontal Lobe and Cognitive Function" (15 min) **Exploring Biological Psychology CD-ROM** "Cortex Puzzle" "The Motor Cortex" "The Sensory Cortex"

CHAPTER 5 *Development and Plasticity of the Brain*

CHAPTER OUTLINE	IDEAS FOR INSTRUCTION	PRINT RESOURCES	MEDIA & INTERNET RESOURCES
Development of the Brain (Module 5.1) • Growth and Differentiation of the Vertebrate Brain • Pathfinding by Axons • Fine-Tuning by Experience • Proportional Growth of Brain Areas • The Vulnerable Developing Brain	**Critical Thinking Exercise** Enriched Environments	**Study Guide** Chapter 5 **Test Bank** Chapter 5 includes approximately 200 multiple-choice items, 30 true/false items, and several essay questions. Also available in **ExamView®** electronic format.	**Multimedia Manager** Create a media lecture for Chapter 5 **WebTutor™ Advantage** Chapter 5 lecture notes, discussion threads, and quizzes on WebCT or Blackboard **Web site** For online quizzes, Web links, and more on Chapter 5, go to: http://psychology.wadsworth.com/book/kalatbiopsych8e/ **InfoTrac® College Edition** *Keywords:* teratogenic, spina bifida **Videos** *Films for the Humanities and Sciences:* "The Development of the Human Brain" (40 min) "Fetal Alcohol Syndrome and Other Drug Use During Pregnancy" (19 min) **Exploring Biological Psychology CD-ROM** "Illustration of Binding" "Sperry Experiment" "Neuroimaging" "Critical Thinking" "Chapter Quiz"
Plasticity After Brain Damage (Module 5.2) • Causes of Brain Damage • Mechanisms of Recovery After Brain Damage • Therapies	**Classroom Activities** Behavioral Effects of Brain Damage An Introduction to Fetal Transplantation **Critical Thinking Exercise** The Kennard Principle		**InfoTrac® College Edition** *Keywords:* brain injury, stroke (subdivision-drug therapy) **CNN® Today Video** "Transplant Therapy for Brain Tumors," Volume 1, Segment 2 (1:35) "Different Brain Injuries," Volume 1, Segment 17 (2:02) **Video** WGBH "Brain Transplant" (1 hour) **Exploring Biological Psychology CD-ROM** "Brains on Ice" "Phantom Limb"

CHAPTER 6 *Vision*

CHAPTER OUTLINE	IDEAS FOR INSTRUCTION	PRINT RESOURCES	MEDIA & INTERNET RESOURCES
Visual Coding and the Retinal Receptors (Module 6.1) • General Principles of Perception • The Eye and Its Connections to the Brain • Visual Receptors: Rod and Cones • Color Vision	**Classroom Activities** Demonstration of the Blind Spot Color Blindness **Critical Thinking Exercise** Color Combinations	**Study Guide** Chapter 6 **Test Bank** Chapter 6 includes approximately 200 multiple-choice items, 30 true/false items, and several essay questions. Also available in ExamView® electronic format.	**Multimedia Manager** Create a media lecture for Chapter 6 **WebTutor™ Advantage** Chapter 6 lecture notes, discussion threads, and quizzes on WebCT or Blackboard **Web site** For online quizzes, Web links, and more on Chapter 6, go to: http://psychology.wadsworth.com/book/kalatbiopsych8e/ **InfoTrac® College Edition** *Keyword:* blindsight **Exploring Biological Psychology CD-ROM** "Virtual Reality Eye" "Blind Spot" "Brightness Contrast" "Color Blindness in Visual Periphery" "Critical Thinking" "Chapter Quiz"
The Neural Basis of Visual Perception (Module 6.2) • An Overview of the Mammalian Visual System • Mechanisms of Processing in the Visual System • Concurrent Pathways in the Visual System • The Cerebral Cortex: The Shape Pathway • The Cerebral Cortex: The Color Pathway • The Cerebral Cortex: The Motion and Depth Pathways • Visual Attention • The Binding Problem Revisited: Visual Consciousness	**Classroom Activity** Gallery of Illusions		**Videos** *Films for the Humanities and Science:* "The Eye: Vision and Perception" (29 min) *Annenberg/CPB:* "Sensation and Perception" (30 min) *Films for the Humanities and Sciences:* "The Mind's Eye: How the Brain Sees the World" (50 min) **Exploring Biological Psychology CD-ROM** "Motion Aftereffect"
Development of the Visual System (Module 6.3) • Infant Vision • Effects of Experience on Visual Development	**Critical Thinking Exercise** Infant Vision		**InfoTrac® College Edition** *Keywords:* cataract, PRK, LASIK, strabismus

CHAPTER 7 *The Other Sensory Systems and Attention*

CHAPTER OUTLINE	IDEAS FOR INSTRUCTION	PRINT RESOURCES	MEDIA & INTERNET RESOURCES
Audition (Module 7.1) <ul><li>Sounds and the Ear</li><li>Pitch Perception</li><li>Hearing Loss</li><li>Localization of Sounds</li></ul>	**Classroom Activity** Can You Hear the Highest Note? **Critical Thinking Exercise** Cochlear Implants	**Study Guide** Chapter 7 **Test Bank** Chapter 7 includes approximately 200 multiple-choice items, 30 true/false items, and several essay questions. Also available in **ExamView®** electronic format.	**Multimedia Manager** Create a media lecture for Chapter 7 **WebTutor™ Advantage** Chapter 7 lecture notes, discussion threads, and quizzes on WebCT or Blackboard **Web site** For online quizzes, Web links, and more on Chapter 7, go to: http://psychology.wadsworth.com/book/kalatbiopsych8e/ **InfoTrac® College Edition** *Keywords:* tinnitus, absolute pitch **CNN® Today Video** "Hearing Loss," Volume 1, Segment 5 (2:04) **Video** *Films for the Humanities and Sciences:* "The Senses: Eyes and Ears" (26 min) **Exploring Biological Psychology CD-ROM** "Hearing Puzzle" "Critical Thinking" "Chapter Quiz"
The Mechanical Senses (Module 7.2) <ul><li>Vestibular Sensation</li><li>Somatosensation</li><li>Pain</li><li>Itch</li></ul>			**InfoTrac® College Edition** *Keywords:* vertigo, intractable pain **Videos** *Annenberg/CPB:* "Phantom Limb Pain" (20 min) *Films for the Humanities and Sciences:* "The Senses: Skin Deep" (26 min) **Exploring Biological Psychology CD-ROM** "Somesthetic Experiment"
The Chemical Senses (Module 7.3) <ul><li>General Issues About Chemical Coding</li><li>Taste</li><li>Olfaction</li><li>Vomeronsal Sensation and Pheromones</li></ul>	**Classroom Activities** Are You a Supertaster? Taste Blindness Gender Differences in Odor Detection		**InfoTrac® College Edition** *Keyword:* aroma therapy **CNN® Today Video** "Taste Changes in Videos," Volume 1. Segment 6 (2:02)
Attention (Module 7.4) <ul><li>Conscious and Unconscious, Attended and Unattended Experience</li><li>Neglect</li><li>Attention-Deficit Hyperactivity Disorder</li></ul>	**Critical Thinking Exercise** Subliminal Thoughts		**InfoTrac® College Edition** *Keyword:* ADHD and Adults **Exploring Biological Psychology CD-ROM** "Attention Deficit Disorder"

23

CHAPTER 8 *Movement*

CHAPTER OUTLINE	IDEAS FOR INSTRUCTION	PRINT RESOURCES	MEDIA & INTERNET RESOURCES
The Control of Movement (Module 8.1) ● Muscles and Their Movements ● Units of Movement	**Classroom Activity** Infant Reflexes **Critical Thinking Exercise** Athletic Ability	**Study Guide** Chapter 8 **Test Bank** Chapter 8 includes approximately 200 multiple-choice items, 30 true/false items, and several essay questions. Also available in ExamView® electronic format.	**Multimedia Manager** Create a media lecture for Chapter 8 **WebTutor™ Advantage** Chapter 8 lecture notes, discussion threads, and quizzes on WebCT or Blackboard **Web site** For online quizzes, Web links, and more on Chapter 8, go to: http://psychology.wadsworth.com/book/kalatbiopsych8e/ **InfoTrac® College Edition** *Keyword:* spasticity **Exploring Biological Psychology CD-ROM** "The Withdrawal Reflex" "The Crossed Extensor Reflex" "Critical Thinking" "Chapter Quiz"
Brain Mechanisms of Movement (Module 8.2) ● The Role of the Cerebral Cortex ● The Role of the Cerebellum ● The Role of the Basal Ganglia	**Classroom Activity** Motor Processing		**InfoTrac® College Edition** *Keywords:* poliomyelitis, ataxia **Exploring Biological Psychology CD-ROM** "Major Motor Areas" "The Brain Pacemaker"
Disorders of Movement (Module 8.3) ● Parkinson's Disease ● Huntington's Disease	**Critical Thinking Exercise** Parkinson's and Aging		**InfoTrac® College Edition** *Keyword:* Parkinson's Disease—surgical division **CNN® Today Video** "Help for the Parkinson's Patients," Volume 1, Segment 4 (1:48) **Videos** *Films for the Humanities and Sciences:* "Advances in Neurology and Neurosurgery" (22 min) *Lippincott, Williams, and Wilkins:* "Common Movement Disorders" (90 min)

CHAPTER 9 *Wakefulness and Sleep*

CHAPTER OUTLINE	IDEAS FOR INSTRUCTION	PRINT RESOURCES	MEDIA & INTERNET RESOURCES

Rhythms of Waking and Sleeping
(Module 9.1)
 	
● Endogenous Cycles
 	
● Mechanisms of the Biological Clock
 	
● Setting and Resetting the Biological Clock
	Classroom Activity
	  Body Temperature and Reaction Time
	
	Critical Thinking Exercise
	  The Night Shift
		Study Guide
		  Chapter 9
		
		Test Bank
		  Chapter 9 includes approximately 200 multiple-choice items, 30 true/false items, and several essay questions. Also available in ExamView® electronic format.
			Multimedia Manager
			  Create a media lecture for Chapter 9
			
			WebTutor™ Advantage
			  Chapter 9 lecture notes, discussion threads, and quizzes on WebCT or Blackboard
			
			Web site
			  For online quizzes, Web links, and more on Chapter 9, go to:
			  http://psychology.wadsworth.com/book/kalatbiopsych8e/
			
			InfoTrac® College Edition
			  Keywords: jet lag, melatonin
			
			Videos
			  Annenberg/CPB: "The Mind Awake and Asleep" (30 min)
			
			  Films for the Humanities and Sciences: "Chronobiology: The Time of Our Lives" (58 min)
			
			Exploring Biological Psychology CD-ROM
			  "Critical Thinking"
			  "Chapter Quiz"

Stages of Sleep and Brain Mechanisms
(Module 9.2)
 	
● The Stages of Sleep
 	
● Paradoxical or REM Sleep
 	
● Brain Mechanisms of Wakefulness and Arousal
 	
● Brain Function in REM Sleep
 	
● Abnormalities of Sleep
			InfoTrac® College Edition
			  Keywords: napping, sleep apnea
			
			Videos
			  Films for the Humanities and Sciences: "Wake Up America: A Sleep Alert" (18 min)
			
			  "Understanding Sleep" (26 min)
			
			  "Sleep Disorders" (50 min)
			
			Exploring Biological Psychology CD-ROM
			  "Sleep Cycle"
			  "EEG"
			  "Awake"
			  "Stage 1"
			  "Stage 2"
			  "Stage 3"
			  "Stage 4"
			  "REM"

Why Sleep? Why REM? Why Dream?
(Module 9.3)
 	
● The Functions of Sleep
 	
● The Functions of REM Sleep
 	
● Biological Perspectives on Dreaming
	Classroom Activity
	  Dream Diaries
	
	Critical Thinking Exercise
	  Developmental Perspective on the Functions of Sleep
			InfoTrac® College Edition
			  Keywords: sleep deprivation, sleep and memory, dreams—analysis subdivision
			
			CNN® Today Video
			  "Sleep Deprived Americans," Volume 1, Segment 9 (1:51)
			
			Video
			  Films for the Humanities and Sciences: "Dreams: Theater of the Mind" (28 min)

CHAPTER 10 *Internal Regulation*

CHAPTER OUTLINE	IDEAS FOR INSTRUCTION	PRINT RESOURCES	MEDIA & INTERNET RESOURCES
Temperature Regulation (Module 10.1) ● Homeostasis ● Controlling Body Temperature	**Critical Thinking Exercise** Living in Extreme Environments	**Study Guide** Chapter 10 **Test Bank** Chapter 10 includes approximately 200 multiple-choice items, 30 true/false items, and several essay questions. Also available in ExamView® electronic format.	**Multimedia Manager** Create a media lecture for Chapter 10 **WebTutor™ Advantage** Chapter 10 lecture notes, discussion threads, and quizzes on WebCT or Blackboard **Web site** For online quizzes, Web links, and more on Chapter 10, go to: http://psychology.wadsworth.com/book/kalatbiopsych8e/ **InfoTrac® College Edition** *Keyword:* fever **Exploring Biological Psychology CD-ROM** "Critical Thinking" "Chapter Quiz"
Thirst (Module 10.2) ● Mechanisms of Water Regulation ● Osmotic Thirst ● Hypovolemic Thirst	**Critical Thinking Exercise** Are Sport Drinks Necessary?		**InfoTrac® College Edition** *Keywords:* dehydration, polydipsia **Exploring Biological Psychology CD-ROM** "Pathways from the Lateral Hypothalamus"
Hunger (Module 10.3) ● How the Digestive System Influences Food Selection ● How Taste and Digestion Control Hunger and Satiety ● The Hypothalamus and Feeding Regulation ● Satiety Chemicals and Eating Disorders	**Classroom Activity** Comparing Eating Disorders with Other Mental Illness		**InfoTrac® College Edition** *Keywords:* appetite depressants, childhood obesity **CNN® Today Video** "Hunger and the Brain," Volume 1, Segment 10 (1:48) "Fat Genes," Volume 1, Segment 11 (1:34) "Wasting Away," Volume 1, Segment 12 (2:58) **Videos** *Insight Media:* "Dying To Be Thin" (60 min) *Films for the Humanities and Sciences:* "Eating Disorders" (26 min)

CHAPTER 11 *Reproductive Behaviors*

CHAPTER OUTLINE	IDEAS FOR INSTRUCTION	PRINT RESOURCES	MEDIA & INTERNET RESOURCES
The Effects of Sex Hormones (Module 11.1) ● Control of Hormone Release ● Organizing Effects of Sex Hormones ● Activating Effects of Sex Hormones ● Parental Behavior	**Critical Thinking Exercise** Gender vs. Sexual Behaviors	**Study Guide** Chapter 11 **Test Bank** Chapter 11 includes approximately 200 multiple-choice items, 30 true/false items, and several essay questions. Also available in ExamView® electronic format.	**Multimedia Manager** Create a media lecture for Chapter 11 **WebTutor™ Advantage** Chapter 11 lecture notes, discussion threads, and quizzes on WebCT or Blackboard **Web site** For online quizzes, Web links, and more on Chapter 11 go to: http://psychology.wadsworth.com/book/kalatbiopsych8e/ **InfoTrac® College Edition** *Keywords:* precocious puberty, castration and sex offenders **Videos** *Films for the Humanities and Sciences:* "Understanding Sex" (51 min) "Sugar and Spice: The Facts Behind Sex Differences" (51 min) **Exploring Biological Psychology CD-ROM** "Menstruation Cycle" "Erectile Dysfunction" "Sex Dysfunction in Women" "Critical Thinking" "Chapter Quiz"
Variations in Sexual Behavior (Module 11.2) ● Evolutionary Interpretations of Mating Behavior ● Determinants of Gender Identity ● Possible Biological Bases of Sexual Orientation	**Classroom Activity** Defining Normal Sexual Behavior **Critical Thinking Exercise** Sexual Orientation		**InfoTrac® College Edition** *Keywords:* hermaphroditism, gay parenting **Videos** *Insight Media:* "Gender and Sexuality" (30 min) *Films for the Humanities and Sciences:* "Homosexuality" (26 min) "The Gay Gene" (30 min)

CHAPTER 12 *Emotional Behaviors*

CHAPTER OUTLINE	IDEAS FOR INSTRUCTION	PRINT RESOURCES	MEDIA & INTERNET RESOURCES
What is Emotion? (Module 12.1) ● Emotions and Decision-Making ● Emotions, Autonomic Arousal, and the James-Lange Theory ● Brain Areas Associated with Emotion	**Critical Thinking Exercise** Does Spock Have Emotions?	**Study Guide** Chapter 12 **Test Bank** Chapter 12 includes approximately 200 multiple-choice items, 30 true/false items, and several essay questions. Also available in ExamView® electronic format.	**Multimedia Manager** Create a media lecture for Chapter 12 **WebTutor™ Advantage** Chapter 12 lecture notes, discussion threads, and quizzes on WebCT or Blackboard **Web site** For online quizzes, Web links, and more on Chapter 12, go to: http://psychology.wadsworth.com/book/kalatbiopsych8e/ **InfoTrac® College Edition** *Keyword:* emotional intelligence (EI) **Exploring Biological Psychology CD-ROM** "Critical Thinking" "Chapter Quiz"
Stress and Health (Module 12.2) ● Stress and the Autonomic Nervous System ● Stress and the Hypothalamus-Pituitary-Adrenal Cortex Axis ● Posttraumatic Stress Disorder	**Classroom Activity** The Polygraph Test: A Reflection of Autonomic System Changes		**InfoTrac® College Edition** *Keywords:* psychoneuroimmunology, stress and memory **CNN® Today Video** "Post-Traumatic Stress and 9/11," Volume 1, Segment 14 (2:40) **Videos** *Films for the Humanities and Sciences:* "Emotion and Illness" (30 min) *Insight Media:* "Stress, Health, and Coping" (30 min) **Exploring Biological Psychology CD-ROM** "Health and Stress" "Stress and Brain"
Attack and Escape Behaviors (Module 12.3) ● Attack Behaviors ● Escape, Fear, and Anxiety	**Classroom Activity** The Obsessive-Compulsive Test **Critical Thinking Exercise** Empathy and the Amygdala		**InfoTrac® College Edition** *Keywords:* panic disorder, anxiety and antidepressants **Videos** *Films for the Humanities and Sciences:* "The Mind of a Killer: Case Study of a Murderer" (26 min) "Circuits of Fear: Anxiety Disorders" (51 min) **Exploring Biological Psychology CD-ROM** "Amygdala and Fear Conditioning" "CNS Depressants"

CHAPTER 13 *The Biology of Learning and Memory*

CHAPTER OUTLINE	IDEAS FOR INSTRUCTION	PRINT RESOURCES	MEDIA & INTERNET RESOURCES
Learning, Memory, Amnesia, and Brain Functioning (Module 13.1) • Localized Representations of Memory • Types of Memory • The Hippocampus and Amnesia • Other Types of Brain Damage and Amnesia	**Classroom Activities** Distinguishing Episodic, Semantic, and Procedural Memories The Mini-Mental Status Examination	**Study Guide** Chapter 13 **Test Bank** Chapter 13 includes approximately 200 multiple-choice items, 30 true/false items, and several essay questions. Also available in ExamView® electronic format.	**Multimedia Manager** Create a media lecture for Chapter 13 **WebTutor™ Advantage** Chapter 13 lecture notes, discussion threads, and quizzes on WebCT or Blackboard **Web site** For online quizzes, Web links, and more on Chapter 13, go to: http://psychology.wadsworth.com/book/kalatbiopsych8e/ **InfoTrac® College Edition** *Keywords:* false memories, memory and imaging **CNN® Today Video** "Alzheimer's Disease and the Brain," Volume 1, Segment 8 (2:05) "Predicting Alzheimer's Disease," Volume 1, Segment 18 (2:13) **Videos** *Insight Media:* "Learning and Memory" (34 min) "Memory" (30 min) **Exploring Biological Psychology CD-ROM** "Classical Conditioning" "Amnestic Patient" "Alzheimer's Patient" "Implicit Memories" "Critical Thinking" "Chapter Quiz"
Storing Information in the Nervous System (Module 13.2) • Blind Alleys and Abandoned Mines • Learning and the Hebbian Synapse • Single-Cell Mechanisms of Invertebrate Behavior Change • Long-Term Potentiation in Mammals	**Critical Thinking Exercises** LTP and Memory Enriched Environments		**InfoTrac® College Edition** *Keyword:* neuroplasticity **Videos** *Insight Media:* "Fires of the Mind" (58 min) *Films for the Humanities and Sciences:* "Memory: Fabric of the Mind" (28 min) **Exploring Biological Psychology CD-ROM** "Long Term Potentiation" "Neural Networks and Memory"

CHAPTER 14 *Lateralization and Language*

CHAPTER OUTLINE	IDEAS FOR INSTRUCTION	PRINT RESOURCES	MEDIA & INTERNET RESOURCES
Lateralization of Function (Module 14.1) ● Visual and Auditory Connections to the Hemispheres ● Cutting the Corpus Callosum ● Development of Lateralization and Handedness ● Avoiding Overstatements	**Classroom Activity** What Hemisphere Are You Using?	**Study Guide** Chapter 14 **Test Bank** Chapter 14 includes approximately 200 multiple-choice items, 30 true/false items, and several essay questions. Also available in ExamView® electronic format.	**Multimedia Manager** Create a media lecture for Chapter 14 **WebTutor™ Advantage** Chapter 14 lecture notes, discussion threads, and quizzes on WebCT or Blackboard **Web site** For online quizzes, Web links, and more on Chapter 14, go to: http://psychology.wadsworth.com/book/kalatbiopsych8e/ **InfoTrac® College Edition** *Keywords:* handedness, cerebral dominance **Videos** *Films for the Humanities and Sciences:* "The Sinister Hand: A Look at Left-Handedness" (28 min) "Man in the Mirror" (60 min) **Exploring Biological Psychology CD-ROM** "Hemisphere Control" "Hemispheric Specialization" "Lateralization and Language" "Critical Thinking" "Chapter Quiz"
Evolution and Physiology of Language (Module 14.2) ● Nonhuman Precursors of Language ● How Did Humans Evolve Language ● Brain Damage and Language ● Dyslexia	**Critical Thinking Exercises** What Is the Function of Language? Gender and Reading Disorders		**InfoTrac® College Edition** *Keywords:* animal communication—subdivision research, dyslexia **Videos** *Films for the Humanities and Sciences:* "Broken English: The Effects of Brain Damage on Language" (47 min) "Chimp Talk" (13 min) "Don't Be Shy, Mr. Sacks: Williams Syndrome" (50 min)

CHAPTER 15 *Psychological Disorders*

CHAPTER OUTLINE	IDEAS FOR INSTRUCTION	PRINT RESOURCES	MEDIA & INTERNET RESOURCES
Substance Abuse (Module 15.1) • Synapses, Reinforcement, and Drug Use • Common Drugs and Their • Synaptic Effects • Alcohol and Alcoholism	**Classroom Activity** Survey on Drug Use/Abuse Patterns **Critical Thinking Exercise** What About Nicotine?	**Study Guide** Chapter 15 **Test Bank** Chapter 15 includes approximately 200 multiple-choice items, 30 true/false items, and several essay questions. Also available in ExamView® electronic format.	**Multimedia Manager** Create a media lecture for Chapter 15 **WebTutor™ Advantage** Chapter 15 lecture notes, discussion threads, and quizzes on WebCT or Blackboard **Web site** For online quizzes, Web links, and more on Chapter 15, go to: http://psychology.wadsworth.com/book/kalatbiopsych8e/ **InfoTrac® College Edition** *Keywords:* drug legalization, Naltrexone and alcoholism, Wernicke's encephalopathy **CNN® Today Videos** "Ecstasy and The Brain," Volume 1, Segment 3 (1:46) "Fighting Addiction," Volume 1, Segment 13 (2:08) **Videos** *Films for the Humanities and Sciences:* "The Addicted Brain" (26 min) "The Hijacked Brain" (57 min) *Insight Media:* "Under the Influence: The Science of Drug Abuse" (25 min) **Exploring Biological Psychology CD-ROM** "Understanding Addiction" "CNS Stimulants" "Opiate Narcotics" "Critical Thinking" "Chapter Quiz"
Mood Disorders (Module 15.2) • Major Depressive Disorder • Bipolar Disorder • Seasonal Affective Disorder	**Classroom Activity** A Self-Rating Depression Scale **Critical Thinking Exercise** Recognizing Bipolar Depression		**InfoTrac® College Edition** *Keyword:* postpartum depression **Videos** *Films for the Humanities and Sciences:* "Depression: Biology of the Blues" (26 min) *Insight Media:* "Bipolar Disorders" (29 min) **Exploring Biological Psychology CD-ROM** "Barbara 1", "Barbara 2" "Mary 1", "Mary 2", "Mary 3"
Schizophrenia (Module 15.3) • Characteristics • Genetics • The Neurodevelopmental Hypothesis • Neurotransmitters and Drugs	**Classroom Activity** Symptoms of Schizophrenia		**InfoTrac® College Edition** *Keyword:* childhood-onset schizophrenia **CNN® Today Video** "Promising Future for a Person With Schizophrenia," Volume 1, Segment 16 (4:33) **Videos** *Films for the Humanities and Sciences:* "Unlocking the Secrets of Schizophrenia" (21 min) *Insight Media:* "Schizophrenia: Causation" (28 min) **Exploring Biological Psychology CD-ROM** "Frontal Neglect and the Wisconsin Card" "Sorting Task" "Etta 1" "Etta 2"

CHAPTER 1

THE MAJOR ISSUES

Chapter Outline

I. **The Mind-Brain Relationship**

   A. **Biological Psychology**: The study of the physiological, evolutionary, and developmental mechanisms of behavior and experience.   Much of biological psychology is devoted to studying how the brain functions.
   B. Biological explanations of behavior fall into four categories:
   1. **Physiological explanations**: Relates behavior to the activity of the brain and other organs. Deals with the machinery of the body.
   2. **Ontogenetic explanations**: Describes the development of a structure or a behavior. Looks at the influence of genes, nutrition, experience, and the interaction among these influences on behavior.
   3. **Evolutionary explanations**: Examines a structure or a behavior in terms of evolutionary history. Examines the continuity (unbroken course) of a behavior from past ancestors to the present.
   4. **Functional explanations**: Describes why a structure or behavior evolved as it did. Looks for the benefit or advantage for having certain behaviors.
   C. The Brain and Conscious Experience
   1. The **mind-body** or **mind-brain problem**: What is the relationship between the mind and the brain?
   2. **Dualism**: The belief that mind and body are different kinds of substances (thought substance and physical substance) that exist independently but somehow interact.
   3. **Monism**: The belief that the universe consists of only one kind of existence. Monism comes in various forms, which primarily fall in the following categories:
       a. **Materialism**: The view that everything that exists is material or physical.
       b. **Mentalism**: The view that only the mind really exists and that the physical world exists only because we think about it.
       c. **Identity position**: The view that mental processes are the same as certain kinds of brain processes, but described in different terms.
   4. Even from the monist position, discussions of consciousness must distinguish the easy problems from the hard problem.
       a. The **Easy problems**: Pertain to the phenomena to which we apply the term consciousness, such as the difference between wakefulness and sleep, and the mechanisms that enable us to focus our attention.
       b. The **Hard problem**: The question of why and how any kind of brain activity is associated with consciousness.
   5. The problem with doing research on mind-body relations is that consciousness is not observable.   We can only infer other people's consciousness.
       a. **Solipsism**: The philosophical position that I alone exist, or I alone am conscious.

b. **The problem of other minds**: The difficulty in knowing whether other people (or animals) have conscious experiences.

II. Nature and Nurture

A. The Genetics of Behavior
1. During the nineteenth century, Gregor Mendel demonstrated that inheritance occurs through **genes** (units of heredity that maintain their identity from one generation to the next).
2. As a rule, genes come in pairs as they are aligned along **chromosomes** (strands of genes). One exception to this rule is sex chromosomes which do not come in pairs.
3. A gene is a portion of a chromosome, which is composed of a double-stranded chemical called **deoxyribonucleic acid (DNA)**.
4. A strand of DNA serves as a template (model) for the synthesis of **ribonucleic acid (RNA)**.
5. RNA is a single-stranded chemical: one type of RNA serves as a template for the synthesis of protein molecules.
6. Proteins can be part of the structure of the body or serve as **enzymes** (biological catalysts that regulate chemical reactions in the body).
7. If individuals have an identical pair of genes on the two chromosomes, they are **homozygous** for that gene; if they instead have an unmatched pair of genes, they are **heterozygous** for that gene (e.g., a gene for black hair on one chromosome and a gene for brown hair on the other).
8. Certain genes can be identified as dominant or recessive.
   a. **Dominant** genes show a strong effect in either homozygous or heterozygous conditions.
   b. **Recessive** genes show their effects only in homozygous conditions (e.g., a carrier for both a black hair gene dominant and a brown hair gene (recessive) will have black hair).
9. In certain cases, the inheritance of one gene is linked to inheritance of another gene. This typically happens when two genes are on the same chromosome.
   a. **Crossing over** is an exception to the linkage of inheritance of genes on the same chromosome where chromosome pairs will break apart and reconnect to each other during reproduction.
10. All mammalian chromosome pairs (with the exception of sex chromosomes) are referred to as **autosomal** chromosomes. Genes located on autosomal chromosomes are **autosomal genes**; genes located on sex chromosomes are **sex-linked genes**.
11. A female mammal has two X chromosomes; a male has one X and one Y chromosome.
12. The Y chromosome carries the gene which causes the person to develop as a male; the X chromosome carries many genes (these are usually referred to as sex-linked genes).
13. Sex-linked recessive genes have their effects only in the absence of the dominant gene.
14. **Sex-limited genes**: Have an effect on one only sex or, at least, a much stronger effect in one sex. Such genes need not be on sex chromosomes and both sexes will

have these genes. The differential effect is because these genes must be activated by sex hormones.

15. Evolution is only possible when variation exists. Two common sources of variation are recombination and mutation.
    a. **Recombination**: A new combination of genes that occurs during reproduction.
    b. **Mutation**: A random change in a single gene; most mutations produce recessive genes.

16. **Heritability**: An estimate of how much of the variance in some characteristic is due to heredity. Heritability ranges from 0 to 1. A heritability of 1 indicates that heredity is responsible for all observed differences; a heritability of 0 indicates heredity is responsible for none of the observed differences.

17. Heritability in humans is studied in two ways. First by comparing monozygotic (identical) twins and dizygotic (fraternal) twins. Second, by comparing adopted children and their biological parents.

18. Heritablility in humans is often overestimated for the following reasons:
    a. Humans tend to share similar environments and the more similar the environment the higher the heritability becomes.
    b. Studies on humans seldom distinguish between genetic and prenatal influences.
    c. **Multiplier effects**: Where small increases in some activity produced by genetic or prenatal effects changes the environment in a way that magnifies that effect.

19. Environmental influences may affect traits with high heritability (e.g., **Phenylketonuria (PKU)**: A genetically caused form of mental retardation that can be avoided with a strict diet that prevents build up of phenylalanine).

20. Genes affect behavior through the proteins they produce and their influence on specific body systems.

B. Evolution of Behavior
    1. **Evolution**: Change over generations in the frequencies of various genes in a population.
    2. While there are still questions about how we evolve (i.e., the process), that we evolve is the inevitable result of how we reproduce. That evolution must occur is based on the following logic:
        a. Offspring generally resemble their parents for genetic reasons.
        b. Mutations and recombinations of genes occasionally introduce new heritable variations.
        c. Some individuals survive longer and produce more than others.
        d. The individuals who reproduce the most pass on the greatest number of genes to the next generation. This new generation will resemble the individuals who reproduced most successfully.
    3. **Artificial-selection**: Breeding animals for desirable individual characteristics (this causes changes in various genetic frequencies in a population).
    4. Misconceptions in evolution:
        a. **Lamarckian evolution**: Use or disuse of some structure or behavior causes an evolutionary increase or decrease in that feature.

      b.   Humans are no longer evolving because of modern medicine and prosperity.

      c.   Evolution means improvement. Actually evolution increases the **fitness** (the number of copies of one's genes that endure in later generations) of the population, but may not give a selective adaptive advantage to later generations.

      d.   Evolution acts to benefit the individual or the species.

5.   **Sociobiology** or evolutionary psychology: The study of the relationship between social behavior and evolutionary theory; sociobiologists emphasize functional explanations of behavior (how a behavior may be useful to a population and why natural selection would favor it). The assumption is that any structure or behavior that is characteristic of the species must have arisen through natural selection (i.e., must be adaptive). It is not known whether this assumption is valid in explaining behavior.

6.   **Altruistic behavior**: Behaviors that benefit others, rather than the individual committing the behavior. This is in contrast to the belief that genes evolve for their own benefit.

      a.   If altruistic genes exist, they may spread through **reciprocal altruism** (the notion that animals help those that help themselves) or **kin selection** (selection in favor of a gene because it benefits the animal's relatives).

III. The Use of Animals in Research

  A. Four reasons why biological psychologists study animal behavior:

    1.   The underlying mechanisms of behavior are similar across species (especially mammalian) and are often easier to study in nonhuman species.

    2.   We are interested in animals for their own sake.

    3.   What scientists learn about animals sheds light on human evolution.

    4.   Certain experiments cannot use human subjects because of legal or ethical restrictions.

  B. The Ethical Debate

    1.   Opposition to animal research ranges considerably in degree.

       "Minimalists" believe some animal research is acceptable, but wish it to be minimized and regulated,

       "Abolitionists" believe that all animals deserve the same rights as human beings and that to use animal subjects is the moral equivalent to slavery and murder.

    2.   Researchers in biological psychology realize that using animals in experiments is necessary for acquiring knowledge about behavior but may indeed be painful to their subjects. Therefore, investigators often look for compromises when conducting animal research to reduce the suffering of animals.

IV. Prospects for Further Study

  A. Research careers (requiring a Ph.D.).

1. *Behavioral neuroscientist* (psychobiologist, biopsychologist, physiological psychologist): Investigates how functioning of the brain and other organs influences behavior.
2. *Neuroscientist*: Studies the anatomy, biochemistry, and physiology of the nervous system.
3. *Neuropsychologist*: Conducts behavioral tests on people with brain damage or brain diseases to determine what the person can and cannot do and to monitor improvement or deterioration over time.
4. *Psychophysiologist*: Measures heart rate, breathing rate, brain waves, and other body processes that change as a function of what someone is doing or what kind of information the person is processing.
5. *Comparative psychologist* (etiologist, animal behaviorist): Compares the behaviors of different species and tries to relate them to evolutionary histories and ecological niches.
6. *Sociobiologist* (evolutionary psychologist): Relates behaviors, especially social behaviors, to the functions they have served and, therefore, the presumed selective pressures that caused them to evolve.

B. Related medical specialties (requiring a MD).
1. *Neurologist*: Treats people with brain damage or diseases of the brain.
2. *Neurosurgeon*: Performs brain surgery.
3. *Psychiatrist*: Helps people with emotional distress or troublesome behaviors, sometimes using drugs or other medical procedures.

Class Activities and Demonstrations

Animal Rights versus Animal Research: This excellent exercise developed by Herzog (1990) mimics the review process that animal research committees undertake when examining proposals for research at colleges and universities. Students are assigned to one of four groups and asked to evaluate a scientific proposal that requires the use of animals; each group must decide whether or not to approve the study and to rate the value and importance of the research. A lively discussion is likely to ensue regarding each group's decisions.

> Source: Herzog, H. (1990). Discussing animal rights and animal research in the classroom. *Teaching of Psychology, 17*, 90-94.

Class Activities and Demonstrations from Selected Web Sites

Evolution—A Historical Perspective. There are some really great activities available on the web (http://www.nap.edu/readingroom/books/evolution98/evol6-g.html) for teaching concepts in evolution. This page was designed by the Working Group for Teaching Evolution under the council of the National Academy of Science primarily for K-12. Review activity seven, which is a fairly sophisticated look at different historical theories in evolution (including Lamarckian and Darwinian theories) and then answer the following questions below.

> Question 1: Compare and contrast Lamarckian and Darwinian theories of evolution. Why is Darwinian theory believed to be a better explanation for the evolution of species?

> Question 2: Explain the key concepts of natural selection. Is the phrase "survival of the fittest" an accurate portrayal of this process?

Class Activities and Demonstrations from Exploring Biological Psychology CD-Rom

Try It Yourself Demonstrations

> Selection and Random Drift

Print Supplements

Study Guide: Chapter 1

Multimedia Resources

VIDEOS

1. How the Human Mind Works: Patricia Smith Churchland (Films for the Humanities and Sciences, 30 min): Dr. Churchland, a professor of philosophy and author of the book *Neurophilosophy*, discusses new theories about how the mind works and about how much control we have over our own thoughts and choices.

2. Is Mind Distinct from Body (Insight Media, 30 min). Examines how Descartes' dualistic view of human nature has been subject to attacks from proponents of materialism, artificial intelligence, and neuroscience.

3. Genetics and Heredity: The Blue Print of Life (Film Ideas, 27 min). Gives a good overview of DNA, meiosis and mitosis, with nice 3-D animation.

4. Hope (Foundation for Biomedical Research, 17 min): Highlights the critical importance of animal research through the eyes of three families. Filmed at Children's National Medical Center in Washington, D.C. Includes Leader's Guide for discussion.

5. Partners in Research (Southwest Association for Education in Biomedical Research, 13 min): Contains interviews with medical researchers, physicians, and patients revealing their thoughts about medical research and the role played by animals. Topics included are medical advances in cystic fibrosis, arthritis, and pediatric diseases.

CD-ROM

Exploring Biological Psychology
> Offspring of parents homozygous and heterozygous for brown eyes (animation)
> RNA, DNA, and protein (animation)
> Critical Thinking (essay questions)
> Chapter Quiz (multiple choice questions)

Related Web Sites

---

http://psychology.wadsworth.com/kalatbiopsych8e

On-line quizzes, weblinks, and more.

http://assc.caltech.edu/

This is the web page of the Association for the Scientific Study of Consciousness. This site provides a lot of interesting information about the history and current research on mind-brain issues.

http://www.accessexcellence.com/AE/AEPC/WWC/1995/

This is from the Woodrow Wilson National Leadership Program in Biology website. They maintain a wonderful web page on the teaching of evolution. There are several laboratory exercises, additional readings, and suggestions for alternative teaching methods.

http://www.indiana.edu/~ensiweb/info.fs.html

This the homepage for ENSI (Evolution and the Nature of Science Institutes). This is another great source for resources on teaching evolution.

http://www.pbs.org/wgbh/evolution/darwin/index.html

This web page was created by the PBS as a part of its Evolution Project. The stated goals of the project are to heighten understanding of evolution and how it works, to dispel common misunderstandings, to illuminate why it is relevant to our lives, to improve its teaching, to encourage a national dialogue, and to prompt participation in all aspects of the project. The web page is an easy to understand wealth of information on Evolution.

http://www.fbresearch.org/

This is the homepage of the Foundation for Biomedical Research. This is an organization that supports the use of animals in biomedical research. Their web page has lots of information about animals in research and good links to other pages.

http://www.sfn.org/

This is the homepage for the Society for Neuroscience. This a really good source for general information about the field of neuroscience and current information about graduate programs in neuroscience.

InfoTrac Key Terms for Class Discussion or Papers

1. **Biofeedback**: Have students research how the mind can learn to control internal systems. Discuss what this means about the separation of mind and body.

2. **Consciousness** (look under subdivision-- research): Have students read how scientists are attempting to study the biological basis of consciousness.

3. **Personality and Genes**: This is a good topic for a paper. Have students write about current research on the genetics of personality and other behavioral attributes.

4. **Animal Rights**: Have students study the philosophical positions of animal advocate groups such as PETA.

Critical Thinking Exercises

The Amazing Tale of Phineas Gage.

The story of Phineas Gage provide a compelling example of the connection between mind and body. Discuss this case with students and have them write brief essays on the mind-body issue. A great overview of the case of Phineas Gage is provided at the Phineas Gage website at http://www.deakin.edu.au/hbs/GAGEPAGE/.

Evolution Versus Technology

Sophisticated genetic testing is on the verge of making it possible to manipulate the genes of a human fetus to determine traits such as height, weight, and body shape. What impact, if any, would you expect from this type of designer genetics on human evolution?

Author's Answers to Thought Questions

1. What would you say or do to try to convince a solipsist that you are conscious?

   I would virtually give up. I would point out that I look and act much like the solipsist, but if he or she isn't inclined to attribute consciousness to me, I cannot demonstrate my inner experience.

2. Now suppose a robot just said and did the same things you did in question 1. Will you be convinced that it is conscious?

   Question 2 is, of course, the reason for my answer to Question 1. For any behavior I might do, I assume it would be possible to build a robot that would do the same thing. (At least I have no justification to rule out the possibility.) But I would not assume that the robot was conscious. (I wouldn't assume that it wasn't conscious, either, for that matter. I simply wouldn't know.)

3. What human behaviors are you sure would have a heritability of 0?

   Probably no behavior has absolute zero heritability, because some genes lead to severe mental retardation, which severely restricts almost any behavior. If we study only people without mental retardation, I would expect zero or very nearly zero heritability for knowledge tests based on information that is available only locally. For example, performance on a test of knowledge about the streets and neighborhoods of Philadelphia would depend mainly on how much time people have spent in Philadelphia. *Which* language one speaks (English, Chinese, etc.)—as opposed to how well one speaks it— presumably has heritability close to zero.

CHAPTER 2

NERVE CELLS AND NERVE IMPULSES

Chapter Outline

I.   **The Cells of the Nervous System**

    A. The Anatomy of Neurons and Glia
        1. The nervous system is composed of two types of cells, neurons and glia.
            a. **Neurons**: cells which receive and transmit information to other cells.
            b. The human brain contains approximately 100 billion neurons.
            c. That the brain like the rest of the body is composed of individual cells was demonstrated by Santiago Ramón y Cajal in the late 1800s.
        2. Neurons contain the same basic structures of other animal cells:
            a. **Membrane** (plasma membrane): Composed of two layers of fat molecules; this membrane allows some small uncharged chemicals to flow both into and out of the cell. *Protein channels* allow a few charged ions to cross the membrane, however most chemicals are unable to cross.
            b. **Nucleus**: The structure that contains the chromosomes.
            c. **Mitochondrion**: The structure that provides cell with energy. Requires fuel and oxygen to function.
            d. **Ribosomes**: Site of protein synthesis in the cell.
            e. **Endoplasmic reticulum**: A network of thin tubes that transports newly synthesized proteins to other locations. Ribosomes may be attached.
        3. The Structure of a Neuron:
            a. The most distinctive structural feature of neurons is their shape.
            b. Most neurons contain four major components: dendrites, cell body, axon, and presynaptic terminal. Small neurons may lack axons and well-defined dendrites. Compare the structure of these components in the following two types of neurons:

                A motor neuron: Conduct impulses to muscles and glands from the spinal cord.

                A sensory neuron (receptor neurons): Sensitive to certain kinds of stimulation (e.g., light, touch, etc.).
            c. Neuron components:

                Dendrites: Branching fibers which extend from the cell body; dendrites receive information (e.g., sensory) from other neurons and send that information to the rest of the neuron.

                Dendritic spines: Short outgrowths found on some dendritic branches.

                Cell body (soma): Contains the nucleus, ribosomes, mitochondria, and other structures found in most cells.

                Axon: A long, thin fiber (usually longer than dendrites) which is the information-sending part of the neuron, sending an electrical impulse toward other neurons, glands, or muscles.

                Myelin sheath: Insulating covering found on some vertebrate axons.

Presynaptic terminal (bouton or end bulb): Swelling at the tip of the axon. Part of the neuron which releases chemicals that cross the junction between one neuron and the next.

 d. Neurons may have any number of dendrites, but are limited to no more than one axon (which may have branches).

 e. Other terms associated with neurons:

Afferent axons: Brings information into a structure.

Efferent axons: Sends information away from a structure.

Interneurons (intrinsic neuron): Entirely located within a single structure of the nervous system.

 f. Variations among neurons:

Neurons vary enormously in size, shape, and function.

A neurons function is closely related to its shape.

A neuron's shape is plastic (changeable) as new experiences can modify the shape of a neuron.

 4. **Glia** (neuroglia):

  a. Glia are the other major component of the nervous system. Glia have many different functions but they do not transmit information like neurons.

  b. A 10:1 ratio of glia to neurons exists in the brain.

  c. **Astrocytes**: A type of glia that absorbs chemicals released by axons and later returns those chemicals back to the axon to help synchronize the activity of neurons. Also, astrocytes remove waste products, particularly those created after neurons die.

  d. **Oligodendrocytes**: A type of glia that builds the myelin sheaths around certain neurons in the brain and spinal cord.

  e. **Schwann cells**: A type of glia that builds the myelin sheaths around certain neurons in the periphery of the body.

  f. **Radial glia**: Type of astrocyte. Guides the migration of neurons and the growth of axons and dendrites during embryonic development.

B. **The Blood-Brain Barrier**: The mechanism that keeps most chemicals out of the vertebrate brain.

 1. The blood-brain barrier is needed because the brain lacks the type of immune system present in the rest of the body.

 2. The blood-brain barrier works because **endothelial cells** forming the walls of the capillaries in the brain are tightly joined blocking most molecules from passing. In the rest of the body the endothelial cells are separated by large gaps.

 3. Small uncharged molecules (e.g., oxygen and carbon dioxide) and molecules that can dissolve in the fats of the capillary wall can cross passively (without using energy) through the blood-brain barrier.

 4. An **active transport** system (a protein-mediated process that uses energy) exists to pump necessary chemicals, such as glucose, through the blood-brain barrier.

C. Nourishment of Vertebrate Neurons

 1. Almost all neurons depend on **glucose** (a simple sugar) for their nutrition.

 2. A **thiamine** (vitamin B_1) deficiency leads to an inability to use glucose, which could lead to neuron death and a condition called Korsakoff's syndrome (a disorder marked by severe memory impairment).

II. The Nerve Impulse

    A. The Resting Potential

        1. The membrane of a neuron maintains an **electrical gradient** (a difference in electrical charge between the inside and outside of the cell).

        2. In the absence of any outside disturbance (i.e., at rest), the membrane maintains an electrical **polarization** (i.e., a difference in electrical charge between two locations) that is slightly more negative on the inside relative to the outside. This difference in electrical potential or voltage is known as the **resting potential**.

        3. The resting potential is measured by very thin *microelectrodes*. A typical resting membrane potential is –70 millivolts (mV).

        4. Forces Acting on Sodium and Potassium Ions:

            a. The neuron membrane has **selective permeability** which allows some molecules to pass freely (e.g., water, carbon dioxide, oxygen, etc.) while restricting others. Most large molecules and ions cannot cross the membrane. A few important ions cross through protein channels.

            b. During the resting potential, potassium and chloride channels (or gates) remain open along the membrane which allows both ions to pass through; sodium gates remain closed restricting the passage of sodium ions.

            c. **Sodium-potassium pump**: a protein complex found along the neuron membrane which transports three sodium ions outside of the cell while also drawing two potassium ions into the cell; this is an active transport mechanism (requires energy to function).

            d. When the membrane is at rest, two forces work on sodium ions:

                The electrical gradient: opposite electrical charges attract, thus sodium (which is positively charged) is attracted to the negative charge inside the cell.

                Concentration gradient (difference in distribution of ions between the inside and the outside of the membrane): Sodium is more concentrated outside the membrane than inside and is thus more likely to enter the cell than to leave it.

                Given that both the electrical and concentration gradients tend to move sodium into the cell, sodium would be expected to quickly enter the cell. However, when the membrane is at rest sodium channels are closed.

            e. Potassium ions are subject to the same two forces, however, the forces are in opposition to each other. Potassium ions are positively charged so the electrical gradient tends to move potassium in, but since potassium is concentrated on the inside of the cell the concentration gradient causes potassium to flow out of the cell.

        5. Why a Resting Potential?

            a. The advantage of the resting potential is to allow the neuron to respond quickly to a stimulus.

    B. The Action Potential

        1. **Hyperpolarization** (increased polarization): Occurs when the negative charge inside the axon increases (e.g., -70mV becomes -80mV).

2. **Depolarization** (reduced polarization towards zero): Occurs when the negative charge inside the axon decreases (e.g., -70mV becomes -55mV).

3. **Threshold of excitation** (threshold): The level that a depolarization must reach for an action potential to occur.

4. **Action potential**: A rapid depolarization and slight reversal of the usual membrane polarization. Occurs when depolarization meets or goes beyond the threshold of excitation.

5. The Molecular basis of the Action Potential

   a. When the potential across an axon membrane reaches threshold, **voltage-activated** (membrane channels whose permeability depends on the voltage difference across the membrane) sodium gates open and allow these ions to enter) this causes the membrane potential to depolarize past zero to a reversed polarity (e.g., -70mV becomes +50mV at highest amplitude of the action potential).

   b. When the action potential reaches its peak, voltage-activated sodium gates close, and potassium ions flow outside of the membrane due to their high concentration inside the neuron as opposed to outside. Also, the electrical gradient is now pushing potassium flow outward.

   c. A temporary hyperpolarization (membrane potential below the resting potential) occurs before the membrane returns to its normal resting potential (this is due to potassium gates opening wider than usual, allowing potassium to continue to exit past the resting potential).

   d. After the action potential, the neuron has more sodium and fewer potassium ions for a short period (this is soon adjusted by the sodium-potassium pumps to the neuron's original concentration gradient).

   e. **Local anesthetic** drugs (e.g., Novocain, Xylocaine, etc.) block the occurrence of action potentials by blocking voltage-activated sodium gates (preventing sodium from entering a membrane).

   f. **General anesthetics** (e.g., ether and chloroform) cause potassium gates to open wider, allowing potassium to flow outside of a neuron very quickly.

   g. Action potentials only occur in axons as cell bodies and dendrites do not have voltage-dependent channels.

6. **All-or-none law**: The size, amplitude, and velocity of an action potential is independent of the intensity of the stimulus that initiated it. If threshold is met or exceeded an action potential of a specific magnitude will occur, if threshold is not met, an action potential will not occur.

7. **Refractory period**: A period immediately after an action potential occurs when the neuron will resist the production of another action potential.

   a. **Absolute refractory period**: Sodium gates are incapable of opening; hence, an action potential cannot occur regardless of the amount of stimulation.

   b. **Relative refractory period**: Sodium gates are capable of opening, but potassium channels remain open; a stronger than normal stimulus (i.e., exceeding threshold) will initiate an action potential.

C. Propagation of the Action Potential

1. The action potential begins at the **axon hillock** (a swelling located where axon exits the cell body).

2. The action potential is regenerated due to sodium ions moving down the axon, depolarizing adjacent areas of the membrane.
3. **Propagation of the action potential**: Transmission (movement) of an action potential down an axon. The action potential moves down the axon by regenerating itself at successive points on the axon.
4. The refractory periods prevent the action potentials from moving in the opposite direction (i.e., toward the axon hillock).

D. Myelin Sheath and Saltatory Conduction
1. **Myelinated axons**: axons covered with a myelin sheath. The myelin sheath is found only in vertebrates and is composed mostly of fats.
2. **Nodes of Ranvier**: Short unmyelinated sections on a myelinated axon.
3. **Saltatory conduction**: The "jumping" of the action potential from node to node.
4. **Multiple sclerosis**: A disease characterized by the loss of myelin along axons; loss of the myelin sheath prevents the propagation of action potentials down the axon.

E. **Local Neurons** (small neuron with short dendrites and a short (if any) axon).
1. Local neurons do not produce action potential but communicate with their closest neighbors using graded potentials (membrane potentials that vary in magnitude and do not follow the all-or-none law). Graded potentials get smaller as they travel.

Class Activities and Demonstrations

---

1. Concentration Gradient: To visually demonstrate how particles will passively move from an area of high concentration to a area of low concentration, add dye to a large container of water and let the color disperse. I have found that a large flask (4 L) and about 1 ml of blue food coloring works very well.

2. Demonstrating the Action Potential: With the use of dominos, explain how the action potential works. Dominos and a stick or thin wooden ruler are required. Arrange dominos in a straight line and tell your students that this represents a neuron. After pushing the first domino, all others fall in sequence: this provides an example of how an action potential begins in one area of a neuron (axon hillock) and travels down the axon. The concept of the refractory period is demonstrated when you can not knock over the dominos again until you reset them. Also, by giving the first domino a slight touch (which is not strong enough to knock it over) you can allow students to conceptualize the all-or-none principle (an action potential will not occur unless the stimulus which creates it forces the neuron to reach it's threshold.)

    Source: Wagor, W.F. (1990) Using dominos to help explain the action potential. In V.P. Makosky, C.C. Sileo, L.G. Whittemore, C.P. Landry, & M.L. Skutley (Eds.) *Activities handbook for the teaching of psychology*: Vol. 3. (pp. 72-73). Washington D.C.: American Psychological Association.

    For smaller classes, an additional exercise for the action potential can also be found in: Reardon, R., Durso, R. T., and Wilson, D. A. (1994). Neural coding and synaptic transmission: participation exercises for introductory psychology. *Teaching of Psychology, 21*, 96-99.

Class Activities and Demonstrations from Selected Web Sites

Neuron slide show: To demonstrate the many unique shapes of neurons in the nervous system supplement the images from the book with images downloaded for the following two web sites: http://class.kmu.edu.tw/~wags/Biology/Wags/histopage/colorpage/cne/cne.htm http://faculty.washington.edu/chudler/gall1.html. After students have viewed the slides, have them discuss the following two questions about neurons.

    Question 1: Is there a relationship between the morphology (shape) and function of a neuron?

    Question 2: Many neuron differ in appearance due to the number of dendrites they have. What would be the advantage to a neuron to have multiply dendrites ?

Class Activities and Demonstrations from Exploring Biological Psychology CD-Rom

---

Virtual Reality Activity

Virtual Reality Neuron

Drag and Drop Exercise

Neuron Puzzle

Print Supplements

Study Guide: Chapter 2

Multimedia Resources

VIDEOS

1. Nerve Impulse Conduction (Insight Media, 29 min): Explores the electrochemical nature of nerve impulses and discusses how certain drugs and chemicals interfere with this process.

2. The Behaving Brain (The Annenberg/CPB Collection, 30 min): This is a good choice for getting students interested in how the brain works. This video includes a simple and easy overview of neuron structure and function. The Behaving Brain is part of the Discovering Psychology series.

CD-ROM

1. Exploring Biological Psychology
   The Parts of a Neuron (animation)
   Resting Potential (animation)
   Action Potential (AP) (animation)
   Action Potential: Na^+ Ions (animation)
   Critical Thinking (essay questions)
   Chapter Quiz (multiple choice questions)

2. The Graphic Brain (Timothy J. Teyler; Brooks/Cole): This CD-ROM provides modules covering many neurophysiological phenomena, such as the movement of ions across an axon membrane, the movement of the action potential along an axon, second-messenger activation, and lateral inhibition as well as other computer-animated presentations.

3. Neurons in Action: Computer Simulations with Neurolab (John W. Moore and Ann E. Stuart; Sinauer Associates): This CD-ROM allows students to perform virtual electrophysiology experiments on neurons. This is great for enhancing students' understanding of the nerve impulses.

Related Web Sites

---

http://psychology.wadsworth.com/kalatbiopsych8e

On-line quizzes, weblinks, and more.

http://psych.hanover.edu/Krantz/neural/actionpotential.html

This sites developed by Dr. John H. Krantz at Hanover College provides an excellent review of the forces involved in the action potential.

http://faculty.washington.edu/chudler/introb.html#bb

This is one of the best resources for teaching basic biological psychology on the web. The site was designed by Dr. Eric Chudler at the University of Washington. It was developed for secondary students, but provides a great overview for both the neuronal structure and neurophysiology discussed in this chapter.

http://pb010.anes.ucla.edu/

This site contains an electronic textbook written by F. Bezanilla called *The Nerve Impulse*. The book gives a thorough overview of the molecular basis of the action potential and other membrane properties.

http://users.rcn.com/jkimball.ma.ultranet/BiologyPages/E/ExcitableCells

This site is from an online biology textbook written by J.W. Kimball. The section on excitable cells gives a concise overview of the signaling properties of neurons.

InfoTrac Key Terms for Class Discussion or Papers

1. **Demyelination**: Have students research the impact of demyelination on motor and sensory systems.

2. **Blood-Brain Barrier**: Discuss the implications of the blood-brain barrier on treating diseases of the brain.

3. **Epilepsy**: After students learn how neurons signal, have them research the consequences of abnormal neuronal signaling.

4. **Neurons** (look under subdivision –growth): Recent evidence suggests that in some parts of the brain, the ability to grow new neurons is retained after birth. Have students research this subject for a paper or oral presentation.

Critical Thinking Exercises

Appreciating Myelin

Have students discuss in class or write on the impact of myelin on the human nervous system. Specifically, have the students decide what behaviors would be impossible if the human nervous system evolved without myelin.

Cocaine

Along with its ability to induce euphoria, cocaine like Novocaine is a local anesthetic. Discuss the effect that systemically administered cocaine could have on the functioning of the nervous system.

Author's Answers to Thought Questions

1. Suppose that the threshold of a neuron were the same as the neuron's resting potential. What would happen? At what frequency would the cell produce action potentials?

   The cell would produce action potentials spontaneously, limited only by the refractory period of the axon. If the cell's refractory period was x (a unit of time), the spontaneous firing rate in action potentials per second would be 1/x.

2. In the laboratory, researchers can apply an electrical stimulus at any point along the axon, making action potentials travel in both directions from the point of stimulation. An action potential moving in the usual direction, away from the axon hillock, is said to be traveling in the *orthodromic* direction. An action potential traveling toward the axon hillock is traveling in the *antidromic* direction. If we started an orthodromic action potential at the axon hillock and an antidromic action potential at the opposite end of the axon, what would happen when they met at the center? Why? What research might make use of antidromic impulses?

   When the two impulses met in the center, both would stop, because the point at which they met would be surrounded on both sides by axon areas in their refractory periods. Here is one way to use antidromic impulses in research: Suppose you are interested in an axon that terminates in one part of the brain, and you want to know where the axon originated. You could electrically stimulate that axon, then record from various places and try to trace the antidromic impulse back to the origin of the axon. Of course, this will be ineffective if the cell has a high spontaneous firing rate, because orthodromic impulses will cancel the antidromic impulses at their point of collison.

3. If a drug partly blocked a membrane's potassium channels, how would it affect the action potential?

   Potassium ions would exit the cell more slowly than usual after an action potential. Therefore, the action potential will be prolonged. In Chapter 13 we shall deal with sensitization, a phenomenon that apparently depends on decreased opening of potassium channels.

CHAPTER 3

COMMUNICATION AT SYNAPSES

Chapter Outline

I. **The Concept of the Synapse**

   A. The Properties of **Synapses** (gaps between neurons where a specialized type of communication occurs).
      1. Sherrington deduced the properties of the synapse from his experiments on **reflexes** (an automatic muscular response to stimuli).
      2. **Reflex arc**: the circuit from sensory neuron to muscle response.
      3. Sherrington discovered that:
         a. Reflexes are slower than conduction along an axon; thus, there must be a delay at the synapse.
         b. Synapses are capable of summating stimuli.
         c. Excitation of one synapse leads to a decreased excitation or inhibition of others.
   B. **Temporal summation**: Repeated stimulation of one **presynaptic neuron** (the neuron that delivers the synaptic potential) occurring within a brief period of time will have a cumulative effect on the **postsynaptic neuron** (the neuron that receives the message).
   C. **Graded potentials**: Either depolarization (excitatory) or hyperpolarization (inhibitory) of the postsynaptic neuron. A graded depolarization is known as an **excitatory postsynaptic potential (EPSP)** and occurs when Na^+ ions enter the postsynaptic neuron. EPSPs are not action potentials: The EPSP's magnitude decreases as it moves along the membrane.
   D. **Spatial summation**: Several synaptic inputs originating from separate locations exerting a cumulative effect on a postsynaptic neuron.
   E. **Inhibitory postsynaptic potential (IPSP)**: A temporary hyperpolarization of a postsynaptic cell (this occurs when K^+ leaves the cell or Cl^- enters the cell after it is stimulated).
   F. **Spontaneous firing rate**: The ability to produce action potentials without synaptic input (EPSPs and IPSPs increase or decrease the likelihood of firing action potentials).

II. **Chemical Events at the Synapse**

   A. In most cases, synaptic transmission depends on chemical rather than electrical stimulation. This was demonstrated by Otto Loewi's experiments where fluid from a stimulated frog heart was transferred to another heart. The fluid caused the new heart to react as if stimulated.
   B. The major events at a synapse are:
      1. Neurons synthesize chemicals called neurotransmitters.
      2. Neurons transport the neurotransmitters to the axon terminal.
      3. Action potentials travel down the axon.

4. At the axon or presynaptic terminal, the action potentials cause calcium to enter the cell which leads to the release of neurotransmitters from the terminal into the *synaptic cleft* (space between the presynaptic and postsynaptic neuron).
5. Neurotransmitters, once released into the synaptic cleft, attach to receptors and alter activity of the postsynaptic neuron.
6. The neurotransmitters will separate from their receptors and (in some cases) are converted into inactive chemicals.
7. In some cells, much of the released neurotransmitter is taken back into the presynaptic neuron for recycling.
8. In some cells, empty vesicles are returned to the cell body.

C. Chemicals released by one neuron at the synapse and affect another neuron are **neurotransmitters**.
D. Types of neurotransmitters include:
   1. **Amino acids**: Acids containing an amine group (NH_2).
   2. **Peptides**: Chains of amino acids. A long chain is called a *polypeptide*; a still longer chain is a *protein*.
   3. **Acetylcholine**: A chemical similar to an amino acid, with the NH_2 group replaced by an $N(CH_3)_3$ group.
   4. **Monoamines**: Nonacidic neurotransmitters containing an amine group (NH_2) formed by a metabolic change of an amino acid.
   5. **Purines**: Adenosine and several of its derivatives.
   6. **Gases**: Includes nitric oxide (NO) and possibly others.
E. Synthesis of neurotransmitters: Neurons synthesize neurotransmitters from precursors derived originally from food.
   1. **Catecholamines** (Dopamine (DA), Epinephrine (E), and Norepinephrine (NE): Three closely related compounds containing a catechol and an amine group.
   2. Choline is the precusor for acetylcholine. Choline is obtained from certain foods or made by the body from lecithin.
   3. The amino acids phenylalanine and tyrosine are precursors for the catecholamines.
   4. The amino acid *tryptophan* is the precursor for serotonin.
F. Transport of Neurotransmitters
   1. Certain neurotransmitters, such as acetylcholine, are synthesized in the presynaptic terminal. However, larger neurotransmitters, like peptides, are synthesized in the cell body and transported down the axon to the terminal.
   2. Transporting neurotransmitters from the cell body to the axon terminal can take hours or days in long axons.
G. Release and Diffusion of Transmitters
   1. Neurotransmitters are stored in **vesicles** (tiny nearly spherical packets) in the presynaptic terminal. (Nitric oxide is an exception to this rule, as neurons do not store nitric oxide for future use). There is also substantial amounts of neurotransmitter outside the vesicles.
   2. When an action potential reaches the axon terminal, the depolarization causes voltage-dependent calcium gates to open. As calcium flows into the terminal, the neuron releases neurotransmitter into the synaptic cleft for 1-2 milliseconds. This process of neurotransmitter release is called **exocytosis**.

3. After being released by the presynaptic neuron, the neurotransmitter diffuses across the synaptic cleft to the postsynaptic membrane where it will attach to receptors.
4. The brain uses dozens of neurotransmitters, but no single neuron releases them all.
5. Each neuron releases the same combination of neurotransmitters at all branches of its axon.

H. Activation of Receptors of the Postsynaptic Cell
   1. A neurotransmitter can have two types of effects when it attaches to the active site of the receptor: ionotropic or metabotropic effects.
   2. **Ionotropic effects**: Neurotransmitter attaches to the receptor causing the immediate opening of an ion gate (e.g., glutamate opens Na^+ gates).
   3. **Metabotropic effects**: Neurotransmitter attaches to a receptor and initiates a cascade of metabolic reactions. This process is slower and longer lasting than ionotropic effects. Specifically, when the neurotransmitter attaches to the receptor it alters the configuration of the rest of the receptor protein; enabling a portion of the protein inside the neuron to react with other molecules. Activation of the receptor by the neurotransmitter leads to activation of G-proteins which are attached to the receptor.
      a. **G-proteins**: A protein coupled to the energy-storing molecule, guanosine triphosphate (GTP).
      b. **Second messenger**: Chemicals that carry a message to different areas within a postsynaptic cell; the activation of a G-protein inside a cell increases the amount of second messenger.
   4. **Neuromodulators**: Neurotransmitters, mainly the peptide neurotransmitters, that do not by themselves strongly excite or inhibit a neuron, instead they alter (modulate) the effects of a neurotransmitter.

I. Inactivation and Reuptake of Neurotransmitters
   1. Neurotransmitters become inactive shortly after binding to postsynaptic receptors. Neurotransmitters are inactivated in different ways.
   2. **Acetylcholinesterase** (AChE): Found in acetylcholine (ACh) synapses; AChE quickly breaks down Ach after it releases from the postsynaptic receptor.
   3. **Myasthenia gravis**: Motor disorder caused by a deficit of acetylcholine transmission. This disease is treated with drugs which block AChE activity.
   4. After separation from postsynaptic receptor, serotonin and the catecholamines are taken up by the presynaptic neuron. This process is called **reuptake**; it occurs through specialized proteins called **transporters**.
   5. Some serotonin and catecholamine molecules are converted into inactive chemicals by enzymes such as **COMT** (converts catecholamines) and **MAO** (converts both catecholamines and serotonin).

J. How Drugs Affect Synapses
   1. Drugs can affect synapses by either blocking the effects (an **antagonist**) or mimicking (increasing) the effects (an **agonist**) of a neurotransmitter.
   2. Drugs can influence synaptic activity in many ways, including altering synthesis of the neurotransmitter, disrupting the vesicles, increasing release, decreasing reuptake, blocking its breakdown into inactive chemical, or directly simulating or blocking postsynaptic receptors.
   3. **Affinity**: How strongly the drug attaches to the receptor.

    4. **Efficacy**: The tendency of the drug to activate a receptor.

K. Synapses and Personality

    1. Synapses are critical for almost all behavior, thus the fact that receptor levels vary in humans may be useful as a genetic marker of personality. Statistically weak correlations have been found for certain types of behavior and dopamine receptors. Specifically, a less common form of the dopamine D_2 receptor which may be less sensitive, has been implicated in risky behaviors such as alcohol consumption, drug use, overeating, and habitual gambling. Similarly, an alternate form of the dopamine D_4 receptor has been associated with a "novelty-seeking" personality.

Class Activities and Demonstrations from Selected Web Sites.

Reaction Time and Neural Circuitry: This exercise is designed to demonstrate the concept of reaction time, the amount of time required for the nervous system to receive and integrate incoming sensory information and then cause the body to respond. The direction for this exercise can be downloaded from http://student.biology.arizona.edu/sciconn/Neuroscience/rxntime.html. After completing the exercise and collecting the data, have students answer the following two questions.

Question 1: Why would reaction time differ between the left and right arm?

Question 2: People differ in their reaction time. Is there any advantage to having a slower than average reaction time?

Print Supplements

Study Guide: Chapter 3

Multimedia Resources

VIDEOS

1. The Electric Ape (Film for the Humanities and Sciences, 58 min): This very colorful video covers how the brain communicates by using electrical and chemical signals. It also demonstrates how these signals are used to process information from the outside world and how they enable us to express ourselves and move.

2. Bubble, Bubble, Toil, and Trouble (Film for the Humanities and Sciences, 58 min): This video discusses how neurons are connected into precise circuits that enable us to sense the outside world. The video covers both simple and complex neuronal circuitry and discusses how communication between neurons can be modified by drugs.

3. The Brain (Film for the Humanities and Sciences, 23 min). The role of chemical neurotransmitters in neuronal communication is highlighted in this video. The film also covers what dreams tell us about brain functioning and how new technologies are being used to study the brain.

CD-ROM

1. Exploring Biological Psychology
    Postsynaptic Potentials (animation)
    Release of Neurotransmitter (animation)
    Cholinergic (animation)
    Release of ACh (animation)
    AChE Inactivates ACh (animation)
    AChE Inhibitors (animation)

Critical Thinking (essay questions)
Chapter Quiz (multiple choice questions)

2. Explorations in Human Anatomy and Physiology (George B. Johnson; Denoyer Geppert International): This CD-ROM contains interactive segments on action potentials, synaptic transmission, and the neurophysiology of drug addiction.

Related Web Sites

http://psychology.wadsworth.com/kalatbiopsych8e

On-line quizzes, weblinks, and more.

http://faculty.washington.edu/chudler/introb.html#bb

This is one of the best resources for teaching basic biological psychology on the web. The site was designed by Dr. Eric Chudler at the University of Washington. He does a good job of making synaptic transmission seem easy.

http://www.williams.edu:803/imput/index.html

Multimedia Neuroscience Education Project, Dr. Betty Zimmerberg (project organizer). Great overview with very nice animation of synaptic transmission.

http://web.indstate.edu/thcme/mwking/nerves.html

This is very detailed overview of the process of synaptic transmission and of the neurotransmitters. The site was designed by Dr. Michael W. King at the University of Indiana Medical School.

http://salmon.psy.plym.ac.uk/year1/neurotr.htm

This is an excellent source of information on synaptic transmission. It is clearly written and and has lots of color and animation. I think most students would find it very interesting. The site was designed by Dr. Paul Kenyon at the University of Plymouth.

InfoTrac Key Terms for Class Discussion or Papers

1. **Reaction Time**: Have students research the role of synaptic integration in reaction time.

2. **Nerve Gas**: Nerve gases work by interfering with acetylcholine inactivation in the synaptic cleft. Students will gain a better appreciation of the importance of inactivation of neurotransmitters by studying nerve gases.

Critical Thinking Exercises

Electrical Synaptic Transmission

Have students discuss how synaptic communication would differ if electrical rather than chemical transmission was used. In particular, have students decide if phenomena like temporal and spatial summation would be possible, and would we still have EPSPs and IPSPs.

Tryptophan

Tryptophan is the amino acid precursor to the neurotransmitter serotonin. It is also an essential amino acid, which means that our bodies are not capable of making this compound. Have students discuss what effects a no tryptophan diet would have on neurotransmission.

Bliss

Pretend a new chemical named Bliss has been found in the central nervous system. Moreover, protein receptors have also been located that interact with this chemical. Is this chemical a neurotransmitter? Have students decide what additional evidence would be necessary before Bliss can be declared a neurotransmitter.

Author's Answers to Thought Questions

1. When Sherrington measured the reaction time of a reflex (that is, the delay between stimulus and response), he found that the response occurred faster after a strong stimulus than after a weak one. How could you explain this finding? Remember that all action potentials-- whether produced by strong or weak stimuli--travel at the same speed along a given axon.

   A strong stimulus induces a greater frequency of action potentials in the sensory axon. Through the process of temporal summation, the next neuron in the sequence can reach its threshold faster if it is stimulated by an increased frequency of synaptic excitation. That is, the reflex is faster with a strong stimulus because of decreased delay of reaching the threshold in the postsynaptic neuron.

2. A pinch on an animal's right hind foot leads to excitation of an interneuron that excites the motor neurons connected to the flexor muscles of that leg; the interneuron also inhibits the motor neurons connected to the extensor muscles of the leg. In addition, this interneuron sends impulses that reach the motor neuron connected to the extensor muscles of the left hind leg. Would you expect the interneuron to excite or inhibit that motor neuron? (Hint: The connections are adaptive. When an animal lifts one leg, it must put additional weight on the other legs to maintain balance.)

   The interneuron excites the extensor muscles of the left hindleg. When the animal flexes one hindleg, it extends the other hindleg.

3. Neuron X has a synapse onto neuron Y, and Y has a synapse onto Z. Presume here that no other neurons or synapses are present. An experimenter finds that excitation of neuron X causes an action potential in neuron Z after a short delay. However, she determines that the synapse of X onto Y is inhibitory. Explain how the stimulation of X might produce excitation of Z.

If the synapse of Y onto Z is also inhibitory, and if neurons Y and Z have spontaneous firing rates, then the excitation of X would inhibit Y and thereby decrease Y's inhibition of Z. The net effect is an increased frequency of action potentials in Z. This sort of inhibition of inhibition is common in the nervous system; thus, there is no consistent relationship between the excitation or inhibition of a synapse and the excitation or inhibition of behavior. Norepinephrine and dopamine are generally inhibitory at their synapses, but drugs that stimulate norepinephrine or dopamine (e.g. amphetamine, cocaine) tend to excite behavioral activity.

4. Suppose that axon A enters a ganglion (a cluster of neurons) and axon B leaves on the other side. An experimenter who stimulates A can shortly thereafter record an impulse traveling down B. We would like to know whether B is just an extension of axon A, or whether A formed an excitatory synapse on some neuron in the ganglion, whose axon is axon B. How could an experimenter determine the answer? You should be able to think of more than one good method. Presume that the anatomy within the ganglion is so complex that you cannot simply trace the course of an axon through it.

There are a number of possibilities.
First, the better methods:
a. Time the transmission of an impulse from a point on A to a point on B and then compare that velocity to the velocity of transmission along A alone or B alone. If the velocity from A to B is slower than the velocity along either axon alone, then there is a synapse between A and B; they are axons of different neurons. If the velocity is the same, then B is an extension of A.
b. Compare axons A and B. If they differ in diameter or in velocity of action potentials, they must be different axons. If they are equal in diameter and velocity, we can draw no conclusion. B might be an extension of A, or the two might be different axons that coincidentally have the same diameter and velocity.
c. Use antidromic conduction, a concept introduced in a previous thought question. Stimulate B and record from A. If stimulation of B produces an antidromic impulse in A, then A and B are almost certainly the same axon (barring the rare, obscure possibility of a two-directional electrical synapse). This procedure fails if A is constantly firing action potentials, which would block transmission of an antidromic impulse.
d. Cut either axon A or axon B. If the other one degenerates, the two must be parts of the same axon. If cutting one does not harm the other, they must be separate axons.
e. Inject a dye into A or B and see whether it spreads to the other. If it does, they are probably the same axon, although a few dyes do cross some synapses. If the dye spreads

through the injected axon but does not invade the other one, then A and B are separate axons.

f. Stimulate A at a high rate and record from both A and B. Synapses fatigue faster than axons, so if A and B are separate, B should stop responding before A does.

Less satisfactory answers:

a. Stimulate other axons entering the ganglion and see whether any of them excites B. If an experimenter finds such an axon, one could conclude that A and B are connected by a synapse. However, failure to find additional axons that stimulate B would not lead to any conclusion.

b. Inject chemicals into the ganglion that facilitate or block various neurotransmitters and see whether they block the effect of A on B. If some chemical does block the transmission to B, then we would not only know that an A-to-B synapse exists, but we would also be able to infer which transmitter it uses. However, if all the chemicals we try have no effect, we could not draw a conclusion. Axon A might release some other transmitter that is not blocked by the chemicals the experimenter tried.

c. "Look for evidence of temporal summation." This is an inappropriate answer, because the question postulated that a single impulse in A is enough to excite B.

5. Transmission of visual and auditory information relies largely on ionotropic synapses. Why would ionotropic be better than metabotropic for these purposes? For what purposes might metabotropic synapses be better?

It is important to detect rapid changes in what we see and hear, and ionotropic synapses produce quick, brief responses. Metabotropic synapses would be better for processes with slow onset and offset, such as hunger, thirst, anger.

CHAPTER 4

ANATOMY OF THE NERVOUS SYSTEM

Chapter Outline

I. Research Methods

A. Describing the structure of the brain is a straightforward endeavor that can be accomplished by examining brain structure under light and electron microscopes or **computerized axial tomography** (i.e., **CT** or **CAT scan**, an x-ray technique that can reconstruct images of the brain on a computer).

B. Understanding how the brain works is more difficult. Most research on brain functioning can be grouped into four categories:
1. Examining the effects of brain damage.
2. Examining the effects of stimulating some part of the brain.
3. Recording what happens in the brain during some kind of behavior.
4. Correlating brain anatomy with behavior.

C. Effects of Brain Damage
1. The French neurologist, Paul Broca, pioneered modern neurology when he discovered that damage to a particular region in the left frontal hemisphere is associated with a loss of the ability to speak. This area of the brain is known as *Broca's area*.
2. Since Broca's discovery, many other researchers have reported behavioral impairments after brain damage. The strategy the researchers use is to describe the brain damage and then examine the brain damage under a microscope after the person dies or through brain scans while the person lives.
3. This type of research is problematic because of a lack of control, as no two people will have exactly the same type of brain damage.
4. An alternative method is to temporarily inactivate a part of the human brain and then study behavior. Brain activity can be interrupted by applying an intense magnetic field over the scalp in the area of interest.
5. In animals, intentional damage to the brain can be produced by implanting electrodes or by injecting certain chemicals. Researchers can also use a **gene-knockout approach** where they direct a mutation to a particular gene that is important for certain types of cells, transmitters, or receptors.
6. After causing damage to an animal's brain, the main problem is to specify exactly how the behavior has changed after the damage.

D. Effects of Brain Stimulation
1. Brain stimulation should increase some behaviors, just as brain damage impairs it.
2. In laboratory animals, brain stimulation can be produced by applying brief electrical stimulation to implanted electrodes; in humans, brain stimulation is accomplished by magnetic fields applied to the scalp. The magnetic fields used to stimulate brain activity are briefer and less intense than those used to interrupt brain activity.

3. The brain can also be stimulated by injecting a chemical that stimulates a particular kind of receptor. However, this type of stimulation will occur wherever the receptor is located, as opposed to stimulating one area of the brain like electrical or magnetic stimulation.

4. Brain stimulation is very useful for understanding behaviors that are solely mediated by a single brain area, such as seeing a flash of light; however, this approach is not as informative for complex behaviors, as they typically involve the coordinated contributions of many brain areas.

E. Recording Brain Activity
   1. In laboratory animals, researchers can record brain activity with electrodes or by removing chemicals from the brain. In humans, brain activity is recorded using noninvasive methods such as:
      a. **Positron emission tomography (PET scan)**: where an investigator injects a radioactive chemical and detectors around the head will map the areas of the brain with the highest level of radioactivity. PET scan can be used to measure brain activity or the binding of a drug to different brain areas.
      b. **Regional cerebral blood flow (rCBF)**: where an investigator injects a chemically inert radioactive chemical that dissolves in the blood, and then uses a PET scanner to measure its distribution in the blood. This technique gives you a measure of regional brain activity.
      c. **Functional magnetic resonance imaging (fMRI)**: a technique that measures changes in the blood's hemoglobin molecules as they release oxygen, mainly in the brain's most active areas. Because fMRI is safer and cheaper than PET, it has replaced PET for many purposes.
   2. One of the most difficult tasks in using these noninvasive methods is interpreting what the images mean. Critical to making an appropriate interpretation is choosing an appropriate comparison task.

F. Correlating Brain Activity with Behavior
   1. Phrenology: process developed by Franz Joseph Gall in the 1800s that related skull anatomy to behavioral capacities.
   2. Today researchers try to relate behavior to measurable features of the brain.

II. Structure of the Vertebrate Nervous System

A. Terminology that Describes the Nervous System
   1. The vertebrate nervous system is comprised of the central nervous system and the peripheral nervous system.
   2. **Central nervous system (CNS)**: Consists of the brain and spinal cord.
   3. **Peripheral nervous system (PNS)**: Consists of the nerves outside the brain and the spinal cord. The PNS has two divisions:
      a. **Somatic nervous system**: Consists of the nerves that convey messages from the sense organs to the CNS and from the CNS to the muscles and glands.
      b. **Autonomic nervous system**: A set of neurons that control the heart, the intestines, and other organs.
   4. Anatomical Terms Referring to Direction
      a. **Dorsal**: towards the back

        b.   **Ventral**: towards the stomach
        c.   **Anterior**: toward the front
        d.   **Posterior**: toward the rear
        e.   **Superior**: above another part
        f.   **Inferior**: below another part
        g.   **Lateral**: toward the side, away from the midline
        h.   **Medial**: toward the midline, away from the side
        i.   **Proximal**: located close to the point of origin or attachment
        j.   **Distal**: located more distant from the point of origin or attachment
        k.   **Ipsilateral**: on the same side of the body
        l.   **Contralateral**: on the opposite side of the body
        m.   **Coronal plane**: plane that shows the brain structures as seen from the front
        n.   **Saggital plane**: plane that shows the brain structures as seen from the side
        o.   **Horizontal plane**: plane that shows brain structures as seen from above

    5.   Terms Referring to Parts of the Nervous System
        a.   **Lamina**: a row or layer of cell bodies separated from other cell bodies by a layer of axons and dendrites
        b.   **Column**: a set of cells perpendicular to the surface of the cortex, with similar properties
        c.   **Tract**: a set of axons within the CNS, also know as a *projection*.
        d.   **Nerve**: a set of axons in the periphery, either from the CNS to a muscle or gland or from a sensory organ to the CNS
        e.   **Ganglion**: a cluster of neuron cell bodies, usually outside the CNS
        f.   **Gyrus** (pl. gyri): a protuberance on the surface of the brain
        g.   **Sulcus**: (pl. sulci): a fold or groove that separates one gyrus from another
        h.   **Fissure**: a long deep sulcus

B.   The **Spinal Cord**: Part of the CNS found within the spinal column; the spinal cord communicates with the sense organs and muscles below the level of the head.
    1.   The spinal cord is a segmented structure. Each segment sends sensory information to the brain and receives motor commands from the brain.
    2.   **Bell-Magendie law**: Dorsal roots enter the spinal cord carrying information from sensory organs (e.g., skin); ventral roots exit the spinal cord carrying motor information to muscles and glands.
    3.   **Dorsal root ganglia**: clusters of sensory neuron cell bodies located outside the spinal cord.
    4.   The **gray matter** lies in the center of the spinal cord, packed with cell bodies and dendrites.
    5.   The **white matter** lies in the periphery of the spinal cord, comprised mainly of myelinated axons.

C.   The **Autonomic Nervous System (ANS)**: is a set of neurons that receives information and sends commands to the heart, intestines, and other organs. The ANS is composed of two divisions:
    1.   **Sympathetic nervous system**: "Fight or Flight" system (prepares body for action by increasing heart rate, blood pressure, etc.). The ganglia for the sympathetic nervous system are near the spinal cord and are closely linked.

2. **Parasympathetic nervous system**: Vegetative nonemergency system (parasympathetic activities are generally opposite of sympathetic activities). The parasympathetic nervous system is also known as the craniosacral system because it consists of cranial nerves and nerves from the sacral spinal cord. The parasympathetic ganglia are not close to the spinal cord. Long *preganglionic* fibers extend from the spinal cord to the ganglia which are located close to the target organs. Short *postganglionic* fibers extend from the ganglia to the nearby organs.

3. Parasympathetic postganglionic fibers release acetylcholine. Most sympathetic postganglionic fibers release norepinephrine, although a few sympathetic postganglionic fibers use acetylcholine.

D. The brain is composed of three major divisions: the hindbrain, the midbrain, and the forebrain.

E. **Hindbrain**: Posterior part of the brain consists of medulla, pons, and cerebellum.

1. **Brainstem**: Consists of the medulla, pons, midbrain, and certain central structures of the forebrain.

2. **Medulla** (medulla oblongata): Controls breathing, heart rate, vomiting, coughing, and other vital reflexes through the **cranial nerves**, a set of twelve nerves that carry sensory and motor information to the head.

3. **Pons** (Latin for "bridge"): Brain structure that lies anterior and ventral to the medulla. Axons in the pons cross from one side of the brain to the other.

4. **Reticular Formation** and **Raphe System** lie in both the pons and medulla.

5. **Cerebellum**: Organizes sensory information which guides movement.

F. **Midbrain**: Middle of the brain

1. **Tectum** (Latin for roof): Comprised of the **superior colliculus** and **inferior colliculus**; both are involved in processing sensory information.

2. **Tegmentum** (Latin for covering): includes III and IV cranial nerve nuclei, part of the reticular formation, and many important pathways.

3. **Substantia Nigra**: Midbrain structure that contains dopamine neurons which degenerate in Parkinson's Disease.

G. **Forebrain**: Most anterior portion and prominent part of the human brain. Consists of cerebral cortex (outer region of the brain) and several subcortical areas:

1. **Limbic System**: Comprised of the olfactory bulb, hypothalamus, hippocampus, amygdala, and cingulate gyrus. The limbic system is involved in motivational and emotional behaviors.

2. **Thalamus**: The thalamus and the hypothalamus form the *diencephalon*. The rest of the forebrain makes up the *telencephalon*. The thalamus provides the main source of information to the cerebral cortex. Most sensory information is first processed in the thalamus before going to the cerebral cortex. The one exception is olfactory information.

3. **Hypothalamus**: Small structure containing many distinct nuclei. Sends messages to the pituitary gland altering its release of hormone. Important for motivated behavior (i.e., eating, drinking, etc.).

4. **Pituitary Gland**: Endocrine (hormone-producing) gland attached to the base of the hypothalamus.

5. **Basal Ganglia**: A group of subcortical structures including the caudate, putamen, and globus pallidus. Deterioration of the basal ganglia is prominent in Parkinson's disease and Huntington's disease.

6. **Basal Forebrain**: Structures in the dorsal surface of the forebrain including the **nucleus basalis**, a key part of the brain's arousal system.

7. **Hippocampus**: A large structure between the thalamus and the cerebral cortex, mostly toward the posterior of the forebrain. This structure is important for new memory storage.

H. The **Ventricles**: Four fluid-filled cavities within the brain. The ventricles consists of two lateral ventricles, one third, and one fourth ventricle.

1. **Central Canal**: Fluid-filled channel in the center of the spinal cord.

2. **Cerebrospinal fluid (CSF)**: The clear fluid found in the ventricles and central canal. The CSF is formed by the *choroid plexus* (cells found inside the four ventricles).

3. **Meninges**: Thin membranes which surround the brain and spinal cord. CSF flows through the spaces between the brain and the meninges.

4. CSF cushions the brain against mechanical shock when the head moves and provides a reservoir of hormones and nutrients for the brain and spinal cord.

5. **Hydrocephalus**: obstruction and accumulation of CSF within the ventricles or in the subarachnoid space. This condition is usually associated with mental retardation.

III. The Cerebral Cortex

A. The forebrain consists of two cerebral hemispheres, one on the left side and one on the right. Each hemisphere receives contralateral sensory information and controls contralateral motor movement.

B. The **cerebral cortex** is the cellular layers on the outer surface of the cerebral hemispheres.

C. The **corpus callosum** and **anterior commissure**: Two bundles of axons that allow the two brain hemispheres to communicate with one another.

D. Organization of the Cerebral Cortex
1. The cerebral cortex contains up to six distinct **laminae** (layers of cell bodies which lie parallel to the surface of the cortex and are separated from each other by layers of fibers).

2. Cells in the cerebral cortex are also arranged in **columns** (cells with similar properties, organized perpendicular to laminae).

3. The cerebral cortex can be divided into four lobes named for the skull bones that lie over them: occipital, parietal, temporal, and frontal.

E. **Occipital Lobe**: Posterior (caudal) portion of the cerebral cortex; part of the visual pathway system
1. **Primary Visual Cortex (Striate cortex)**: Most posterior region of the occipital lobe. Destruction of any part of the striate cortex causes *cortical blindness*.

F. **Parietal Lobe**: Lies between the occipital lobe and the **central sulcus** (one of the deepest grooves in the surface of the cortex).

1. **Postcentral Gyrus** or **Primary Somatosensory Cortex**: Lies posterior to the central sulcus; the primary target for touch sensations and information from muscle-stretch receptors and joint receptors.
2. The pariental lobe monitors all the information about eye, head, and body positions and passes it on to brain areas that control movement.

G. **Temporal Lobe**: Located laterally in each hemisphere, near the temples; it is the primary target for auditory information.
   1. In humans the left hemisphere temporal lobe is involved in comprehension of spoken language and contributes to complex aspects of vision, including perception of movement and recognition of faces.
   2. The temporal lobe is also implicated in emotional and motivated behaviors.
      Klüver-Bucy syndrome: Set of behaviors seen after temporal lobe damage. Previously wild and aggressive monkeys fail to show normal fear or anxiety.

H. **Frontal Lobe**: Located at the most anterior area of the cerebral cortex and extends to the central sulcus. Contains the primary motor cortex and prefrontal cortex.
   1. **Precentral Gyrus** (also known as the *primary motor cortex*): Located just anterior to the central sulcus. Specialized for the control of fine motor movements, primarily on the contralateral side of the body.
   2. **Prefrontal Cortex**: The most anterior portion of the frontal lobe. Forms a large portion of the brain in large-brained species. Receives information from all of our senses.
   3. **Prefrontal lobotomy**: Disconnecting the prefrontal cortex from the rest of the brain to control psychological disorders. This practice was almost completely abandoned after effective drug therapies became available.
      a. Prefrontal lobotomies commonly resulted in a loss of the ability to plan and take initiative, memory disorders, distractibility, and a loss of emotional expression. In addition, people with prefrontal damage lose their social inhibitions and often acted impulsively.

I. Modern View of Functions of the Prefrontal Cortex
   1. The prefrontal cortex is now believed to be important for *working memory* (the ability to remember recent stimuli and events).
   2. **Delayed-Response Task**: A subject must remember where a stimulus (e.g., toy) was hidden prior to the introduction of a time delay; damage to the prefrontal cortex leads to deficits on this task.
   3. The prefrontal cortex is also believed to be important for context-dependent behaviors.

J. How Do the Parts Work Together
   1. **The Binding Problem** (or large-scale integration problem): The question of how the visual, auditory, and other areas of your brain influence one another to produce a combined perception of a single object.
   2. Early researchers thought the association areas were used for processing and linking the information from several sensory modalities. Later studies demonstrated that association areas do not process information from different sensory areas, but rather provide more elaborate processing for one sensory area.
   3. One hypothesis is that the binding of perception depends on simultaneous activity in various brain areas.

Class Activities and Demonstrations

1. External Sheep Brain Structure: The gross anatomy of the sheep's brain is very similar to the human brain. Studying sheep brains will allow students to better understand how their own brains are organized. For this demonstration you will need sheep brains, which can be purchased from Carolina Sciences, a sheep brain atlas (there is an online sheep atlas available at http://www.uofs.edu/sheep/framerow.html), trays, and disposable gloves. This demonstration works best if you have students work in pairs and have a sheep brain for each pair.

2. Human Brain Structure: This is an excellent and very simple demonstration which enables students to conceptualize the structure of the brain.
Have students place their fingers beneath each ear lobe on both sides of their head. Mention to them that the brainstem, the oldest part of the brain, faces each palm of their hands. Now ask them to make a fist with each hand. State that each brain hemisphere is about the size of one fist. When both fists are joined at the heel of each hand, they approximate the size, shape, and symmetrical structure of the brain. Finally, ask the students to put on a pair of gloves (preferably a gray color) and make a fist. These represent the cerebral cortex, the newest part of the brain, which is responsible for our highest cognitive abilities such as those involving art, language, and problem solving.

   Source: Ornstein, R., & Thompson, R.F. (1984). *The Amazing Brain*. Boston: Houghton Mifflin.

3. Demonstration of the Sensory Homunculus: This demonstration requires students to work in pairs.

   Pair students up, with one assigned as the experimenter and the other as the subject. The experimenter should apply two fingers to the subject's back while the subject is either blindfolded or looking away. Does the subject report feeling one finger or two pressed against his back? Next, the experimenter should press two fingers against the subject's shoulder, back arm, and palm. Compare differences in perception of these body regions. Sensitive body areas, such as the palms of our hands, have more nerve endings in them and more brain sensory area devoted to them. Can students think of reasons why we should appreciate this difference in body sensitivity?

   Source: Motiff, J.P. (1987). Physiological Psychology: The sensory homunculus. In V.P. Makosky, L.G. Whittemore, and A.M. Rogers (Eds.). *Activities handbook for the teaching of psychology*: Vol. 2. (pp. 51-52). Washington, D.C.: American Psychological Association.

Class Activities and Demonstrations from Selected Web Sites

Mapping the Motor Cortex. This web site, http://www.pbs.org/wgbh/aso/tryit/brain/#, is part of the PBS series, A Science Odyssey, which describes the progress in science and technology over the last 100 years. The web site gives a brief overview of the scientists and the experiments that lead to the mapping of the human motor cortex. It also has a neat virtual operation activity where students get to use a probe to stimulate the motor cortex of a human brain. Read the sections entitled *Mapping the Human Brain: a History* and *Wilder Penfield maps the brain*, perform the brain probe activity, and then answer the questions below.

Question 1: The areas mapped by probing the motor cortex do not correspond to actual body size. Speculate on why this occurs?

Question 2: The motor cortex was mapped in the mid 20th century. Why are there so few other areas in the brain mapped.

Class Activities and Demonstrations from Exploring Biological Psychology CD-ROM

Virtual Reality Activity

Virtual Reality Head Planes
Virtual Reality Brain

Drop and Drag Exercise

Planes Puzzle
Cortex Puzzle
Brain Puzzle

Print Supplements

Study Guide: Chapter 4

Multimedia Resources

CNN® Today Video

1. New Brain Research, Volume 1, Segment 1 (2:41 min).

VIDEOS

1. Brain and Nervous System: Your Information Superhighway (Films for the Humanities and Sciences, 31 min): Program explores the brain and nervous system, using the analogy of computers and the internet. The film covers parts of the brain and their function, as well as a general overview of how the brain communicates.

2. The Frontal Lobe and Cognitive Function (The Annenberg/CPB Collection, 15 min): This video module provides an excellent example of a patient with behavioral deficits due to frontal lobe damage. Also included is a discussion of the delayed-response task. (From the series The Mind, Episode 8 "Thinking")

3. Anatomy of the Human Brain (Film for the Humanities and Sciences, 35 min): This video features a prominent neuropathologist, Dr. Marco Rossi, removing, dissecting, and examining a normal human brain.

CD-ROM

1. Exploring Biological Psychology
   - Left Hemisphere Function #1 (roll over with text pop-ups)
   - Saggittal Section: Right Hemisphere #1 (roll over with text pop-ups)
   - Saggittal Section: Right Hemisphere #2 (roll over with text pop-ups)
   - Saggittal Section: Right Hemisphere #3 (roll over with text pop-ups)
   - The Motor Cortex (animation)
   - The Sensory Cortex (animation)
   - Critical Thinking (essay questions)
   - Chapter Quiz (multiple choice questions)

2. Human Anatomy CD-Rom (Gold Standard Multimedia). This is an excellent source for students who wish to visualize human brain dissections with interactive anatomy illustrations. Students also have the opportunity to quiz themselves to test their knowledge on many aspects of the human nervous system.

Related Web Sites

http://psychology.wadsworth.com/kalatbiopsych8e

On-line quizzes, weblinks, and more.

http://faculty.washington.edu/chudler/introb.html#bb

Dr. Chudler's web page gives an easy to follow, but thorough, overview of the central nervous system.

http://www9.biostr.washington.edu/da.html

This is an interactive brain atlas from the Digital Anatomist Project developed at the University of Washington. This site has clear and easy-to-read brain images that allow you to see the brain with or without labels. The images are also available in CD-ROM form.

http://www.vh.org/Providers/Textbooks/BrainAnatomy/BrainAnatomy.html

Brain atlas from real human dissections created by the University of Iowa, College of Medicine. This is a very complete brain atlas.

http://brainmuseum.org/index.html

This is a excellent collection of mammalian brains from many different species. This a great web page for comparing and contrasting human and animal neuroanatomy. The collection is from University of Wisconsin and Michigan State Comparative Mammalian Brain Collections, as well as from those at the National Museum of Health and Medicine. The preparation of these images and specimens was funded by the National Science Foundation, as well as by the National Institutes of Health.

InfoTrac Key Terms for Class Discussion or Papers

1. **Lie Detector**: The extremely fast response of the autonomic nervous system is the basis of lie detecting machines. Have students research the different types of measurements used (e.g., blood pressure, galvanic skin response) in lie detection and debate whether these machines can actually detect lying.

2. **Hydrocephalus**: Hydrocephalus or water on the brain is a disorder where fluids (i.e., CSF) accumulate in the brain. Have students investigate the different causes of the fluid build-up and discuss why the accumulation of fluid is so damaging to brain tissue.

3. **Brain Imaging**: Have students research the different technologies available for non-invasive imaging of the brain. Have students examine the advantages and disadvantages of these technologies.

Critical Thinking Exercises

Measuring Brain Activity

Most of the noninvasive imaging methods estimate brain activity by changes in blood flow, oxygen consumption, glucose utilization, etc. Discuss the potential problems with using this type of indirect measure.

Working Memory vs. Short-Term Memory

The prefrontal cortex has been implicated in working memory. How does the concept of working memory differ from short-term memory? Is it possible to distinguish between these concepts experimentally.

Author's Answers to Thought Questions

1. Certain unusual structural aspects were observed in the brain of Albert Einstein. One interpretation is that he was born with neural features that encouraged his scientific and intellectual abilities. What is an alternative interpretation?

Another possibility is that his many years of scientific work led to specialized growth of certain brain areas. Yet another important possibility is that we are looking at a coincidence: If researchers looked hard enough at any brain, they could no doubt find some structural peculiarity, which might or might not have anything to do with that person's behavioral abilities, inabilities, or quirks.

2. The drug phenylephrine is sometimes prescribed for people suffering from a sudden loss of blood pressure or other medical disorders. It acts by stimulating norepinephrine synapses, including those that constrict blood vessels. One common side effect of this drug is goose bumps. Explain why. What other side effects might be likely?

    Most postganglionic synapses of the sympathetic nervous system use norepinephrine as their transmitter, so phenylephrine will stimulate most of the sympathetic nervous system, including those responsible for erecting the hairs. Other likely side effects would include other sympathetic responses, such as increased heart rate and decreased salivation and digestion.

3. When monkeys with Klüver-Bucy syndrome pick up lighted matches and snakes, we do not know whether they are displaying an emotional deficit or a difficulty identifying the object. What kind of research might help answer this question?

    Here is one possibility: Compare the ability of visual cues and other cues to function as fear stimuli. On some trials present a complex visual stimulus followed by shock; on other trials present an auditory or somatosensory or olfactory stimulus followed by shock. Later, test the ability of each stimulus to elicit a conditioned emotional response. If the monkeys are less responsive to visual stimuli than are intact monkeys with the same training, but equally responsive to the auditory and other stimuli, then their deficit is in interpretation of visual stimuli. However, if they respond weakly to all the stimuli, then their deficit is in emotional responsiveness.

CHAPTER 5

DEVELOPMENT AND PLASTICITY OF THE BRAIN

Chapter Outline

I. **The Development of the Brain**

   A. Growth and Differentiation of the Vertebrate Brain
     1. The human central nervous system begins to form when the embryo is about 2 weeks old.
     2. A neural tube forms around a fluid-filled cavity; this structure eventually sinks under the skin surface and develops into the hindbrain, midbrain, and forebrain. The fluid-filled cavity becomes the central canal and the four ventricles.
     3. The human brain weighs approximately 350 grams at birth and around 1,000 grams at one year of age. The average adult brain weighs between 1,200 and 1,400 grams.
   B. Growth and Development of Neurons
     1. The five steps of neuron development:
       a. **Proliferation**: Production of new cells; cells along the ventricles of the brain divide to become neurons and glia.
       b. **Migration**: Movement of primitive neurons and glia toward their final destination in the brain.
       c. **Differentiation**: Neurons develop an axon and dendrites (this distinguishes neurons from other cells in the body); the axon grows before the dendrites, while the neuron is migrating toward its destination.
       d. **Myelination**: Glia cells produce myelin sheaths around axons which allow for rapid transmission. In humans, myelin forms first in the spinal cord before forming in the brain. Myelination begins during the prenatal period and continues into adulthood.
       e. **Synaptogenesis**: Formation of synapses. This is the last step in neural development and continues throughout life.
   C. Determinants of Neuron Survival
     1. While working on the sympathetic ganglion, Rita Levi-Montalcini discovered that muscles that synapse with the axons from the ganglia don't determine how many neurons are produced but which synapses survive.
     2. She discovered that muscles produce and release **nerve growth factor (NGF)**, which promotes the survival and growth of axons.
     3. Axons that don't receive enough NGF degenerate and their cell bodies die. All neurons are born with this suicide program and will automatically die if the right synaptic connection is not made. This programmed cell death is call **apoptosis**.
     4. **Neurotrophin**: a chemical (like NGF) that promotes the survival and activity of neurons. In addition to NGF, the brain also uses *brain-derived neurotropic factor (BDNF)* as a neurotrophin. Neurotrophins work in several ways. They:
       a. Prevent apoptosis early in development
       b. Increase axonal branching after new experiences later in development

        c.   Increase regrowth of axons after brain damage

    5.   Initially, all areas of the developing nervous system produce two or three times as many neurons than will survive into adulthood.

        a.   The existence of extra neurons allows for errors during development to be corrected (i.e., if some axons do not reach their targets, others will).

        b.   Extra neurons also allow the CNS to compensate for unpredictable body size variations.

D.   Chemical Pathfinding by Axons

    1.   Sperry (1943) discovered that severed optic nerve axons will grow back to their original targets in the tectum. He showed that this process was dependent on chemical gradients in the target cells by severing the optic nerve and rotating the eye by 180°.

    2.   For example, TOP_{DV} is a protein 30 times more concentrated in the axons of the dorsal retina as opposed to ventral retina neurons, and is 10 times more concentrated in the ventral tectum as opposed to the dorsal tectum. Retinal axons and tectal cells with high concentrations of TOP_{DV} connect to each other; those with the lowest concentrations do likewise.

E.   Competition Among Axons as a General Principle

    1.   Postsynaptic cells strengthen the synapses of some cells and weaken synapses with others.

    2.   **Neural Darwinism**: During development, synapses form randomly before a selection process keeps some and rejects others (this is only partly accurate since synapse formation is also influenced by chemical guidance and trophic factors).

F.   Fine-tuning by Experience

    1.   Because of the unpredictability of life, we have evolved the ability to redesign our brain (within limits) in response to experience.

    2.   Effects of Experience on Dendritic Branching

        a.   Environmental enrichment leads to a thicker cortex, more dendritic branching and improved performance on learning tasks in rats.

        b.   Much of the benefit of enriched environments in rats is simply due to exercise; as exercise causes the release of neurotrophins.

        c.   Enriched environments enhance sprouting of axons and dendrites in a wide variety of species including humans.

    3.   Generation of New Neurons

        a.   In contrast to early beliefs, the adult vertebrate brain is capable of developing new neurons.

        b.   Undifferentiated cells, called **stem cells,** can form new glia cells or neurons. Stem cells have been found in the brains of many adult vertebrates, including songbirds, black-capped chickadees, and in some mammals. However, scientists are unclear whether adult primates are capable of producing new neurons.

    4.   Effects of Experience on Human Brain Structures

        a.   Extensive practice of a particular skill makes a person more adept at that skill. In a few cases, researchers have identified brain changes that are associated with increased expertise at a particular skill. For example:

       b.   The auditory cortex response to pure tones is twice as large for professional musicians as for nonmusicians. Moreover, a part of the temporal cortex was found to be 30% larger in professional musicians.

       c.   Violin players have a larger area devoted to the left fingers in the postcentral gyrus than nonmusicians.

5. Combinations of Chemical and Experiential Effects
   a. The evidence discussed so far suggests a two-stage process for making synaptic connections. First axons find approximate targets by following chemical gradients then they strengthen or discard some connections based on experience.
   b. This generalization has exceptions as some axons produce spontaneous action potentials when first reaching their destinations. In the lateral geniculate these action potentials are important for deciding what synaptic connections are appropriate.

G. Proportional Growth of Brain Areas
   1. The human brain is remarkably similar to other species. For instance, nearly all our the neurotransmitters found in the human brain are found throughout the animal kingdom. The ion channels found in our neurons are nearly the same as found in other species including bacteria. The structures of the human brain have nearly the same locations, functions, and detailed anatomies as those of other mammals and has substantial similarities to all vertebrates.
   2. The human brain is larger than most mammals, but is smaller than those of whales, dolphins, or elephants.
   3. **Primates** (monkeys, apes, and humans) have a larger cerebral cortex, in comparison to the rest of the brain then insectivores.
   4. Some differences in brain area size are based on way of life. For instance, bats depend on echolocation and have an unusually large auditory cortex, and monkeys that use their forelimbs to swing through trees have a larger than usual brain representation of muscle and sense organs in the forelimbs.
   5. The development of any brain area depends on two factors: how long the embryological development of the brain lasts in days, and the number of new neurons produced per day.

H. The Vulnerable Developing Brain
   1. Compared to the mature brain, the developing brain is more vulnerable to malnutrition, toxic chemicals, and infections.
   2. **Fetal alcohol syndrome (FAS)**: Caused by alcoholic consumption during pregnancy. Symptoms include decreased alertness, hyperactivity, facial abnormalities, mental retardation, motor problems, and heart defects.
   3. Prenatal exposure to cocaine can lead to slight decreases in IQ scores and somewhat greater decreases in language skills.
   4. Prenatal exposure to cigarette smoking is associated with:
      a. low birth weight and other illness early in life
      b. Sudden Infant Death Syndrome (SIDS)
      c. long-term intellectual deficits
      d. Attention Deficit Hyperactivity Disorder (ADHD)
      e. impairment of the immune system

f.   delinquency and crime later in life (males especially)

II.   Plasticity After Brain Damage

A.   Causes of Human Brain Damage
   1.   **Closed head injury**: A sharp blow to the head that does not actually puncture the brain. The most common cause of brain damage in young people.
      a.   Closed head injuries damage the brain because of rotational forces that drive the brain tissue against the inside of the skull.
   2.   Reducing the harm from a stroke
      a.   **Stroke (cerebrovascular accident)**: A temporary loss of blood flow to the brain. This is a common cause of brain damage, especially in the elderly.
         •   **Ischemia**: The most common type of stroke; loss of blood flow caused by a blood clot or other obstruction of an artery.
         •   **Hemorrhage**: Less common type of stroke, bleeding due to the rupture of an artery.
         •   Strokes destroy neurons in two waves. First, cells in the immediate vicinity of the stroke die almost immediately. Second, cells in the **penumbra** (the area that surrounds the immediate damage) may die over the next few days.
         •   Neurons in the penumbra die after a stroke because potassium ions (which accumulate outside neurons due to a dysfunctional sodium-potassium pump) and **edema** (fluid accumulation) cause glia cells to release glutamate and other neurotransmitters. The excess glutamate overstimulates neurons, because sodium, calcium, and zinc ions build up inside them, causing the membrane to swell or even burst.
         •   Decreasing cell death after a stroke can be accomplished by administering **tissue plasminogen activator (tPA)** clot-busting drugs, that restore blood flow following ischemia or by using drugs that antagonize glutamate activity.
         •   However, researchers have discovered that the most effective method for decreasing cell death in animals is to lower brain temperature from 37°C degrees to 29°C within 30 minutes after the ischemic episode occurs.
   3.   Effects of Age on Recovery
      a.   The elderly do not recover from brain damage as well as younger adults.
      b.   **Kennard principle**: Recovery from brain damage early in life is more extensive than after similar damage later in life.
      c.   The Kennard principle has many exceptions, as young brains are also more vulnerable to forces that interfere with its development and organization.
B.   Mechanisms of Recovery:
   1.   People with brain damage generally show some behavioral improvement after the damage. This recovery is due to structural changes in the surviving neurons and learned changes in behavior.
   2.   Learned Adjustments in Behavior
      a.   Much of the recovery after brain damage is learned; the individual makes better use of unimpaired abilities. A brain-damaged person or animal may also

learn to use abilities that at first appear lost, but are only impaired. For example:

- Monkeys with a **deafferented** (loss of sensory or afferent nerves from a body part) limb fail to use it because walking on three limbs is apparently easier than trying to move the impaired limb. However, if forced they can learn to use the deafferented limb.

3. **Diaschisis**: Decreased activity of surviving neurons after other neurons are destroyed. Behavioral deficits due to diaschisis can sometimes be improved with the use of stimulant drugs.

4. Regrowth of Axons
   a. Damaged axons rarely regenerate in the mammalian central nervous system possibly because of too much scar tissue, which acts a mechanical barrier, and the secretion of growth-inhibiting chemicals called *chrondroitin sulphate proteoglycans*.
   b. Another explanation for the failure of axons to regenerate is that myelin in the CNS of mammals and birds secretes proteins that inhibit axon growth. In contrast, the myelin of the PNS secretes chemicals that sustain axon growth.

5. Sprouting
   a. **Collateral sprouts**: A newly formed branch from an uninjured axon attaches to a synapse vacated when the original axon was destroyed. Sprouting is a normal condition, as the brain is constantly losing old synapses and sprouting new ones to replace them.

6. **Denervation supersensitivity**: Heightened sensitivity to a neurotransmitter after the destruction of incoming axons. Heightened sensitivity as a result of inactivity by an incoming axon is called **disuse supersensitivity**.
   a. Injecting **6-hydroxydopamine (6-OHDA)** into the brain to remove dopamine synapses is one way to demonstrate denervation supersensitivity. After an injection of 6-OHDA, which destroys dopamine neurons, postsynaptic cells react to the decreased dopamine input by increasing their number of dopamine receptors. If 6-OHDA is only injected on the left side, amphetamine (which increases dopamine release) will activate the right intact side and will result in movement on the left. If **apomorphine** (a morphine derivative that directly stimulates dopamine receptors) is given, the movement will be to the right as the receptors on the left will be supersensitized.

7. Reorganization of Sensory Representations and the Phantom Limb
   a. Monkeys that had an entire limb deafferented twelve years previously had a large portion of their cerebral cortex (which was previously responsive to that limb) become responsive to the face. It was later found that amputation of a limb results in axonal sprouts forming not only in the cortex, but also in the spinal cord, brainstem and thalamus.
   b. Brain scans confirm that this process leads to a **phantom limb**, a continuing sensation of an amputated body part.

C. Therapies
   1. Behavioral Interventions

        a.   At present, behavioral therapy consists mainly of supervised practice of impaired behaviors. The therapist tries to help the brain-damaged person find their lost skills or learn to use remaining abilities more effectively.

2. Drugs
   a. Several drugs have aided recovery from brain damage in animals, so far we do not know their effect on humans.
      - **Nimodipine** is a drug that prevents calcium from entering cells.
      - **Gangliosides** (a class of glycolipids—combined carbohydrates and fat molecules) promote restoration of damaged neural tissue.
      - **Progesterone** (a hormone found primarily in women) promotes recovery of frontal cortex damage in female rats.

3. **Brain grafts**: Replacing dead brain cells with healthy donor cells. This technique has been used most frequently in Parkinson's disease, but is still in the experimental stage.

Class Activities and Demonstrations

Behavioral effects of brain damage: A good way for students to understand and appreciate the effects of nervous system damage is to simulate a clinical rounds seminar. Invite a neurologist or neuropsychologist to your class to perform neurological examinations on patients suffering from motor disorders (e.g., Parkinson's disease, multiple sclerosis, myasthenia gravis, etc.). Allow students to ask questions of the physician and patients regarding the variety of drug treatments available for these disorders, their side effects, and the prognosis for a full recovery.

Class Activities and Demonstrations from Selected Web Sites

An introduction to fetal tissue transplantation: This exercise was developed by Rod Harris, Ellen Mayo, and Jim Tankersley for the 1992 Woodrow Wilson Biology Institute.   In this activity, students take a pretest on their views of fetal tissue transplantation and then are given research assignments to complete. After the students complete the assigned research, they will discuss their findings with the class and will take a posttest on their views. To generate discussion ask the class the following questions after completing the exercise.
http://www.accessexcellence.org/AE/AEPC/WWC/1992/fetaltissue_transplants.html

> Question 1: What is the success rate for this type of surgery? Is the prognosis better with tissue transplants than with conventional treatment?

> Question 2: What are the ethical implications of using fetal tissue? Are there viable alternatives to fetal tissue for transplants?

Class Activities and Demonstrations from Exploring Biological Psychology CD-ROM

Try It Yourself Demonstration

> Illustration of Binding

Print Supplements

Study Guide: Chapter 5

Multimedia Resources

CNN® Today Video

1. Transplant Therapy for Brain Tumors, Volume 1, Segment 2 (1:35 min).
2. Different Brain Injuries, Volume 1, Segment 17 (2:02 min).

VIDEOS

1. The Development of the Human Brain (Films for the Humanities and Sciences, 40 min): Examines the formation and growth of the human brain from conception to the moment of birth. Video also follows the child to the age of eight to witness the appearance of a wide range of motor and cognitive functions.

2. Fetal Alcohol Syndrome and Other Drug Use During Pregnancy (Films for the Humanities and Sciences, 19 min): An overview of the brain abnormalities and behavioral deficits associated with fetal alcohol syndrome focusing on Native American populations. The video also covers deficits in children born to cocaine-addicted moms.

3. Brain Transplant (WGBH Educational Foundation, 60 min): This "Nova" episode chronicles the journey of two individuals as they undergo brain graft surgeries for the treatment of MPTP-induced Parkinson's disease.

CD-ROM

Exploring Biological Psychology
   Neuroimaging (video)
   Brains on Ice (video)
   Sperry Experiment (animation)
   Phantom Limb (animation)
   Critical Thinking (essay questions)
   Chapter Quiz (multiple choice questions)

Related Web Sites

http://psychology.wadsworth.com/kalatbiopsych8e

   On-line quizzes, weblinks, and more.

http://www.med.unc.edu/embryo_images/

   Embryo Images online was developed by Dr. Kathleen K. Sulik and Dr. Peter R. Bream Jr. from the University of North Carolina at Chapel Hill. This site has great images of mouse and human embryos at different points of development.

http://www.asntr.org/

   The American Society for Neurotransplantation and Repair (ASNTR) is a society composed of basic and clinical neuroscientists who utilize transplantation and related technologies to better understand the way the nervous system functions and establish new procedures for its repair in response to trauma or neurodegenerative disease. This is a good site for finding the latest research on treatment for brain damage

http://www.merck.com/pubs/mmanual/section14/sec14.htm

An online version of the Merck Manual of Diagnosis and Therapy. This manual has a comprehensive listing of neurological disorders and current treatments.

InfoTrac Key Terms for class discussion or papers

1. **Teratogenic**: Have students research the various chemicals that can lead to abnormal development. Students are particularly interested in the teratogenic effects of abused drugs.

2. **Spina Bifida**: Spina bifida is a common neural tube defect. Have students discuss the life-long consequences of having this disorder to patients. Also have students discuss the research indicating that spina bifida can be prevented by folic acid.

3. **Brain Injury**: Have students research the many ways the brain can sustain an injury.

4. **Stroke** (subdivision-drug therapy): New drugs hold the promise that injury after stroke can be greatly reduced. Have students study the latest drugs used to limit stroke damage.

Critical Thinking Exercises

The Kennard Principle

The recovery from brain damage in the young is more complicated than the Kennard Principle would suggest. Have students discuss the reasons why brain damage in the young may have a worse recovery than in adults. Also, have students discuss whether conventional treatment for brain damage would be useful in a developing brain.

Enriched Environments

The human brain is able to increase synaptic connections in response to early environmental stimulation. Have students discuss how this knowledge could be used to improve our educational system and improve academic performance.

Author's Answers to Thought Questions

1. Biologists can develop antibodies against nerve growth factor (that is, molecules that inactivate nerve growth factor). What would happen if someone injected such antibodies into a developing nervous system?

   Without nerve growth factor, a developing axon degenerates and its cell body dies. After an injection of antibodies to NGF, many neurons would probably die.

2. Based on material in this chapter, what is one reason why a woman should avoid long-lasting anesthesia during delivery of a baby?

   The developing brain is more vulnerable than the adult's. Prolonged exposure to anesthetic drugs can increase apoptosis in the brain of a fetus or infant.

3. Ordinarily, patients with Parkinson's disease move very slowly, if at all. However, during an emergency (such as a fire in the building) they sometimes move rapidly and vigorously. Suggest a possible explanation.

   The emergency situation increases arousal, somewhat like injecting amphetamine into the body, and thereby increases activation of dopamine and norepinephrine synapses.

4. Drugs that block dopamine synapses tend to impair or slow limb movements. However, after people have taken such drugs for a long time, some experience involuntary twitches or tremors in their muscles. Based on something in this chapter, propose a possible explanation.

   Prolonged inactivity at a synapse can produce disuse supersensitivity, with a larger number of receptors or increased efficiency of receptors. By blocking dopamine synapses for a long time, the drugs cause the dopamine receptors to overrespond to small amounts of dopamine, perhaps even to spontaneous release of it.

CHAPTER 6

VISION

Chapter Outline

I. **Visual Coding and the Retinal Receptors**

    A. General Principles of Perception
        1. Each receptor is specialized to absorb one kind of energy and transduce it into an electrochemical pattern in the brain.
        2. Visual receptors absorb and can respond to as little as one photon of light. The light is then transduced into a **receptor potential**, a local depolarization or hyperpolarization of a receptor membrane. The strength of the receptor potential determines the amount of excitation or inhibition the receptor delivers to the next neuron.
        3. From Neural Activity to Perception
            a. Rene Descartes believed that the brain's representation of a physical stimulus had to resemble the stimulus itself, so that when you look at something the nerves from the eye would project a picture like pattern onto your visual cortex. The problem with this theory is that it assumes that there is a little person in the head who can look at the picture.
            b. It is now known that coding of visual information in your brain does not duplicate the shape of the object you see.
        4. Law of Specific Nerve Energies
            a. **Law of specific nerve energies**: any activity by a particular nerve always conveys the same kind of information to the brain. In other words, the brain sees the activity of the optic nerves and hears the activity of the auditory nerve.
            b. In immature ferrets, researchers rerouted the optic nerve on one side of the brain away from its normal thalamic target onto a thalamic target that usually gets input from the ears. They found that the formerly auditory thalamus and cortex reorganized to process visual information.
            c. Cells can signal one kind of stimulus by an increase in firing rate and a different signal with a decrease in firing rate.
    B. The Eye and Its Connections to the Brain
        1. **Pupil**: An opening in the center of the *iris* (a band of tissue that give our eyes their color) in which light enters the eye. The pupil is focused by the lens (adjustable) and cornea (not adjustable) and projected to the retina.
        2. **Retina**: Rear surface of the eye which is lined with visual receptors.
        3. Light from the left side of the world strikes the right half of the retina and vice-versa; light from below strikes the top half of the retina and vice-versa.
        4. The Route within the Retina
            a. Within the vertebrate retina, receptors, send their messages to **bipolar cells** (neurons located close to the center of the eye).

      b.   Bipolar cells send their message to **ganglion cells** (neurons located even closer to the center of the eye).

      c.   *Amacrine cells* get information from bipolar cells and send it to other bipolar cells, other amacrine cells, or ganglion cells. They are important for complex processing of visual information.

      d.   The ganglion cells join together to form the **optic nerve** (or optic tract). The point at which the optic nerve leaves the eye is known as the **blind spot,** because it has no visual receptors.

    5.   The Fovea and Periphery of the Retina

      a.   *Macula*: Portion of the retina with the greatest ability to resolve detail.

      b.   **Fovea**: Central portion of the macula specialized for acute, detailed vision. The fovea has the least impeded vision, as blood vessels and ganglion cells are almost absent. Further aiding the detailed vision of the fovea, each receptor connects to a single *bipolar cell* which in turn connects to a single *ganglion cell.*

      c.   Midget ganglion cells: the ganglion cells in humans and other primates. These cells are small and each receives a input from a single cone.

      d.   Each cone in the fovea has a direct line to the brain and can register the exact location of any point of light on the fovea.

      e.   The peripheral regions of the eye have a greater number of receptors for each bipolar cell compared to the fovea and cannot discern fine detail. However, peripheral vision has greater sensitivity to light.

      f.   In many bird species the eyes occupy most of the head, compared to 5% of the head in humans. These birds have two foveas per eye to enhance perception of detail in the periphery.

      g.   The density of receptors in the retina may depend on the needs of the organism. For instance, hawks have a greater density of receptors in the top half of the retina to see below while flying, while rats have a greater density in the bottom half of the retina to locate predators above them.

C. Visual Receptors: Rods and Cones

    1.   Two types of receptors exist in the vertebrate retina: **rods** and **cones**. Rods are abundant in the periphery of the retina; they are involved in both peripheral and night vision. Cones are found primarily in the fovea; they are involved in both visual acuity and color vision.

    2.   Rods and cones contain **photopigments** (chemicals that release energy when struck by light). Photopigments consist of 11-*cis*-retinal bound to proteins called opsins.

D. Color Vision:

    1.   Color vision requires comparing the responses of different kinds of cones. Animals like rats, which have one type of cone, cannot discriminate one color from another.

    2.   In the human visual system, the shortest visible wavelengths (about 400 nm), are perceived as violet; progressively longer wavelengths are perceived as blue, green, yellow and red near 700 nm.

    3.   Color vision requires a special coding system in the nervous system. Two major interpretations of color vision were proposed in the 1800s: the trichromatic theory and the opponent-process theory.

4. **Trichromatic (Young-Helmholtz) Theory:** According to this theory of color vision, humans have three different types of cones, each sensitive to a different set of wavelengths. This theory was based on older research using **psychophysical observations** (reports by observers concerning their perceptions).

5. Opponent-Process Theory
   a. **Negative color afterimages**: visual phenomena that occur when you stare at a colored object under a bright light without moving your head and then look at a plain white surface. You would see a replacement of the red you had been staring at with green, green with red, yellow and blue with each other, and black and white with each other.
   b. To explain negative color afterimages and other visual phenomena the **opponent-process theory** was proposed. According to this theory we perceive color in terms of paired opposites: white-black, red-green and yellow-blue.
   c. Opponent-process theory states that negative afterimages result from fatiguing a response by opponent-process cells (e.g., a cell which responds to green light becomes fatigued after prolonged stimulation, which results in a red afterimage when the green light is removed).

6. Retinex Theory
   a. **Color Constancy**: The ability to recognize the color of objects despite changes in lighting. This ability is not explained by the trichromatic theory or the opponent-process theory.
   b. **Retinex Theory:** Theory proposed to account for color constancy. When information from various parts of the retina reaches the cortex, the cortex compares each of the inputs to determine the brightness and color perception for each area.

7. **Color Vision Deficiency** (color blindness): The inability to perceive color differences as most people do. Red-green color blindness is the most common form of this disorder (primarily seen in males).

II. The Neural Basis of Visual Perception

A. An Overview of the Mammalian Visual System
   1. Rods and cones make synaptic connections with **horizontal cells** and bipolar cells. Horizontal cells make inhibitory contact onto bipolar cells, which in turn synapse with *amacrine* cells and ganglion cells. All these cells are in the eye.
   2. Axons of the ganglion cells from each eye form the optic nerves; the optic nerves from the left and right eyes meet at the optic chiasm where in humans half of the axons from each eye cross to the opposite side of the brain. Most of the ganglion cell axons go to the **lateral geniculate nucleus** (LGN) of the thalamus. Most axons from the LGN synapse in the visual areas of the cerebral cortex.

B. Mechanisms of Processing in the Visual System
   1. Receptive Fields
      a. **Visual Field:** The area of the world that you can see at any time.
      b. The portion of the visual field to which any neuron responds is that neuron's **receptive field.**

2. **Lateral inhibition** (the reduction of activity in one neuron by activity in neighboring neurons): A technique of the retina to sharpen the boundaries of visual objects.

C. Concurrent Pathways in the Visual System
    1. In the Retina and Lateral Geniculate
        Most primate ganglion cells are either **parvocellular neurons** (small cell bodies located in or near the fovea), **magnocellular neurons** (larger cell bodies distributed evenly throughout the retina), or **koniocellular** neurons (similar in size to parvocellular neurons, but distributed throughout the retina).
        a. Parvocellular neurons have small receptive fields and respond best to visual details and color. These cells synapse only onto cells of the LGN.
        b. Magnocellular neurons have larger receptive fields and respond best to moving stimuli. Most of these cells synapse onto cells of the LGN, but a few connect to other areas of the thalamus
        c. Koniocellular neurons have several different functions and their axons connect to the LGN, other areas of the thalamus, and the superior colliculus.
    2. In the Cerebral Cortex
        a. Most axons from the LGN go first to the **primary visual cortex** (also known as area **V1** or *striate cortex*). This area of the cortex is responsible for the first stage of visual processing. Area V1 sends information to the **secondary visual cortex** (area **V2**) which is responsible for the second stage of processing. The connections between V1 and V2 are reciprocal.
        b. In the cortex, the parvocellular and magnocellular pathways split from two pathways into the following three pathways:
            *   A mostly parvocellular pathway sensitive to details of shape.
            *   A mostly magnocellular pathway with a ventral branch sensitive to movement and a dorsal branch that is important for integrating vision with action.
            *   A mixed parvocellular and magnocellular pathway sensitive to brightness and color.
        c. **Ventral Stream:** The parvocellular and magnocellular pathways sensitive to shape, movement, and color-brightness that lead to the temporal cortex. These pathways are also called the "what" pathways because there are specialized for identifying and recognizing objects.
        d. **Dorsal Stream:** The mostly magnocellular pathway associated with intergrating vision and movement that leads to the parietal cortex. This pathway is the "where" or "how" pathway as it helps the motor system find objects, move toward them, grasp them, and so forth.

D. The Cerebral Cortex: The Shape Pathway
    1. David Hubel and Torsten Wiesel distinguished three categories of neurons in the visual cortex: simple, complex and end-stopped or hyper-complex cells.
        a. **Simple cells:** Neurons with fixed excitatory and inhibitory zones in their receptive fields; these cells are found only in the primary visual cortex (V1). Most simple cells have bar-shaped or edge-shaped receptive fields.
        b. **Complex cells:** Located in either V1 or V2, these neurons have receptive fields which respond to particular orientations of light but cannot be mapped into

fixed excitatory and inhibitory zones. Complex cells receive their input from a combination of simple cells.

c. **End-stopped (hyper-complex)** cells: Strongly resemble complex cells but in addition, have an inhibitory area at one end of its bar-shaped receptive field.

2. Cells in the visual cortex are grouped together in columns perpendicular to the surface according to their responsiveness to specific stimuli. For example, cells in a particular column may respond only to visual input from the left, right, or both eyes about equally. Also, cells in some columns respond best to stimuli of a single orientation.

3. **Feature Detectors**: Neurons whose responses indicate the presence of a particular feature. It is believed that some cortical neurons in V1 respond best to spatial frequencies.

4. **Inferior Temporal Cortex**: Neurons in this brain region provide information about complex shaped stimuli (e.g., hands or face). The area is important for **shape constancy** (the ability to recognize an object's shape even as it approaches, retreats, or rotates.

5. Disorders of Object Recognition

a. **Visual agnosia**: The inability to recognize objects despite otherwise normal vision; **prosopagnosia** is the inability to recognize faces without an overall loss of vision or memory.

b. fMRI studies have show that the fusiform gyrus of the inferior temporal cortex is largely specialized for face recognition. The fusiform gyrus is also activated when identifying car models, bird species, and so forth.

E. The Cerebral Cortex: The Color, Motion, and Depth Pathways

1. Color perception depends mostly on the parvocellular and koniocellular pathways.

2. *Blobs*: Patches of cells highly sensitive to color in areas of V1. These cells include parvocellular and koniocellular neurons for color perception and magnocellular cells for brightness perception. The blobs send their output to areas V2, V4, and the posterior inferior temporal cortex.

3. Area V4, and other nearby brain regions, are believed to be important for color constancy. Area V4 also contributes to visual attention.

4. Many of the cells in the magnocellular pathway appear specialized for **stereoscopic depth perception** (the ability to detect depth by differences in what the two eyes see).

5. Area **MT** (middle-temporal cortex, also known as area **V5**) and area **MST** (medial superior temporal cortex) are important for motion detection.

6. Areas MT and MST receive direct input from the magnocellular pathway and some parvocellular input. The mangnocellular pathway detects overall patterns including movement over large areas of the visual field, while the parvocellular pathway detects the disparity between the views of the left and right eye, an important cue for to distance.

7. Cells in the MT respond selectively to a stimulus moving in a particular direction and somewhat to still photographs that imply movement. Cells in the MST respond best to the expansion, contraction, or rotation of a large visual scene.

8. The brain has mechanisms to distinguish between moving objects and visual changes due to head movements. Neurons in the MST respond differentially to eye

movement versus moving objects, and the visual cortex has decreased activity during eye movements.

9. Damage to, or around, area MT results in people becoming **motion blind** (inability to determine where objects are moving or even if they are moving).

F. Visual Attention

1. The difference between attended and unattended stimuli is a matter of the amount and duration of activity in a cortical area.
2. Activation and feedback to area V1 is necessary for attention or conscious awareness of a stimulus.

G. The Binding Problem Revisited: Visual Consciousness

1. The hypothesis that all binding requires precise synchrony of activity in different brain areas is supported by visual processing experiments that show that synchronized activity in two hemispheres is necessary in order to see something that crosses the midline of vision as a single object.
2. A limited amount of visual processing takes place without it being conscious. Some people with extensive damage to area V1 (i.e., cortical blindness) have **blindsight** which means they can localize visual objects although they have a blind visual field.

III. Development of the Visual System

A. Human infants have better visual abilities than once imagined, as infants spend more time looking at faces, circles, or stripes than at patternless displays. Infants, however, have trouble shifting their gaze from one object to the next until approximately 6 months of age.

B. Effects of Experience on Visual Development

1. Effects of Early Lack of Stimulation of One Eye
   a. Most neurons in the visual cortex of cats and primates receive **binocular** input (stimulation from both eyes).
   b. If a kitten is deprived of light stimulation of one eye early in life, the kitten will become almost blind in the deprived eye.

2. Effects of Early Lack of Stimulation of Both Eyes
   a. If both eyes are deprived of stimulation, cortical cells will remain responsive (albeit sluggishly) to both eyes.
   b. People who have abnormal visual development, such as being born blind and then regaining vision, have trouble learning to identify shapes and objects. These people often find their newly gained vision almost useless.
   c. **Sensitive** or **critical period**: A stage of development when experiences have a particularly strong and long-lasting influence. The effects of abnormal experiences on cortical development are dependent on the length of the sensitive period. The length of sensitive periods varies from species to species and from one part of the cortex to another and depends on the availability of the neurotransmitter GABA.
   d. The duration of a sensitive period in humans is unknown but even brief abnormal experience can result in visual deficits. For example, people born

with cataracts (cloudy lenses) and had them surgically repaired at ages 2-6 months still have subtle problems processing complex visual information.

3. Restoration of Response After Early Deprivation of Vision
   a. Research in kittens has demonstrated that sensitivity to a deprived eye can be restored if normal experiences begin soon enough.
   b. **Lazy Eye** or **Amblyopia:** Condition in which a child ignores the vision in one eye, sometimes even letting it drift in a different direction from the other eye. This disorder is treated by putting a patch over the active eye, forcing the child to use the ignored eye. This treatment is based on earlier research in kittens.

4. Uncorrelated Stimulation in Both Eyes
   a. Almost every neuron in the human visual cortex responds to approximately corresponding areas of both eyes.
   b. **Retinal disparity**: Discrepancy between what the left eye sees versus the right. Retinal disparity is necessary for stereoscopic depth perception. The fine-tuning of binocular vision depends on experience.
   c. **Strabismus** (strabismic amblyopia): Condition in which the eyes do not point in the same direction. Individuals born with this disorder cannot perceive depth better with two eyes as opposed to one.
   d. Visual experience promotes the responsiveness of cortical neurons by releasing nerve growth factor (NGF), which promotes the survival of synaptic connections.

5. **Astigmatism**: A blurring of vision for lines in one direction; this disorder is caused by an asymmetric curvature of the eyes. Corrective lenses during early childhood (before ages 3-4 years) improve visual capacity in adulthood.

6. If animals grow up without seeing movement they will become motion blind.

7. Certain portions of the visual cortex in people who are blind early in life become responsive to auditory or touch stimuli.

Class Activities and Demonstrations

Color Blindness: The Ishihara Color Blindness Test Book (Denoyer-Geppert International) contains 14 test plates consisting of patterns of colored dots which are perceived differently by color-blind individuals than by persons with normal vision. These plates can be used as a fascinating class activity to discover what percentage of male class members' vision is affected.

Class Activities and Demonstrations from Selected Web Sites

The Gallery of Illusions from Eric Chuldler's Neuroscience for Kids web page. This activity is a collection of interactive visual illusions. Students will be able to observe the illusion then move around parts of the display to demonstrate that their perception was incorrect. It is an excellent way to lead into a discussion on cortical processing of visual information. The web page can be assessed at http://faculty.washington.edu/chudler/flash/nill.html. Have the student review the illusions then answer the questions below.

Question 1: At what level of visual processing is a visual illusion created?

Question 2: How are blind spots and visual illusions related?

Class Activities and Demonstrations from Exploring Biological Psychology CD-ROM

Virtual Reality Activity

Virtual Reality Eye

Try It Yourself Activities

Motion Aftereffect
Brightness Contrast
Blind Spot
Color Blindness in Visual Periphery

Print Supplements

Study Guide: Chapter 6

Multimedia Resources

VIDEOS

1. The Eye: Vision and Perception (Insight Media, 29 min): This program overviews the structure and function of the mammalian eye and demonstrates how visual receptors work. The video also describes a number of visual disorders and techniques for correcting them.

2. Sensation and Perception (The Annenberg/CPB Collection, 30 min): This program demonstrates how visual information is gathered and processed, and how our perceptions are influenced by our culture, previous experiences, and interests. (From the series Discovering Psychology, Episode 7)

3. The Mind's Eye: How the Brain Sees the World (Films for the Humanities and Sciences, 50 min): Examines the processing of form, color, depth, and motion visual information by examining patients with rare forms of brain damage.

CD-ROM

Exploring Biological Psychology
   The Retina (animation)
   Critical Thinking (essay questions)
   Chapter Quiz (multiple choice questions)

Related Web Sites

---

http://psychology.wadsworth.com/kalatbiopsych8e

On-line quizzes, weblinks, and more.

http://www.accessexcellence.org/AE/AEC/CC/vision_background.html

How We See: The First Steps of Human Vision is from the Access Excellence Classic Collection. This is an easy to follow overview of the anatomy and functions of the eye. The web page also has some neat activities on vision.

http://www.brainconnection.com/topics/?main=anat/receptive-inter

Interactive receptive field mapping activity. This activity is on the Brain Connection.com web page maintained by Scientific Learning corporation. The activity lets you determine the receptive fields for simple bipolar cells and complex cells such as on-center and off-center cells. There is also general information on eye anatomy and physiology.

http://www.michaelbach.de/ot/index.html

A comprehensive collection of visual illusions with explanations. This web site was created by Dr. Michael Bach at the University of Augenklinik.

http://www.nlm.nih.gov/medlineplus/visiondisordersblindness.html

Comprehensive site for information on vision disorders and blindness. This web site is part of MEDLINEplus, a service of the U.S. National Library of Medicine and the National Institutes of Health.

InfoTrac Key Terms for Class Discussion or Papers

1. **Cataract**: A cataract is the loss of transparency of the lens of the eye. Have students research the effects of a cataract on visual abilities.

2. **Photorefractive Keratectomy (PRK)** and **Laser In Situ Keramileusis (LASIK)**: These are two new surgical procedures that reshape the eye to improve visual acuity. Have students debate the pros and cons of this type of procedure.

3. **Blindsight**: Have students study the causes of blindsight and discuss how this visual ability differs from visual abilities processed in the cortex. This is an good place to discuss the role of consciousness and sensory abilities.

4. **Strabismus**: Strabismus is a disorder where the two eyes can not move together. Have students research the techniques used to treat strabismus and why it is so important to treat this disorder early in development.

Critical Thinking Exercises

Infant Vision

The majority of infant crib toys are produced in pastel shades such as light blue or pink. Based on research on the visual abilities of newborns, have the class discuss the colors and designs for toys that would stimulate the infant visual system.

Color Combination

Based on the theories of color vision, is there a biological reason why some color combinations look better than other color combinations? Have the class discuss whether color combinations are based on the biology of the eye or environmental influences. Based on their hypotheses, have them discuss experimental methods for testing the bases of color combination preferences.

Author's Answers to Thought Questions

1. How could you test for the presence of color vision in a bee? Examining the retina will not help; invertebrate receptors resemble neither rods nor cones. It is possible to train bees to approach one visual stimulus and not another. The difficulty is that if you trained some bees to approach, say, a yellow card and not a green card, you would not know whether they solved the problem by color or by brightness. Because brightness is different from physical intensity, you cannot equalize brightness by any physical measurement, nor can you assume that two colors that are equally bright to humans are also equally bright to bees. How might you get around the problem of brightness to study the possibility of color vision in bees?

One could train bees to approach, say, a blue card to get food. One then wants to test whether the bees select the card on the basis of color or on the basis of brightness. One puts down a large array of cards, one blue and many grays varying as widely as possible in brightness. If the bees select the blue card from among all the grays, they must have color vision. An experiment using this procedure successfully demonstrated color vision in bees: Karl von Frisch (1953). *The Dancing Bees*, New York: Harcourt Brace & World.

2. After a receptor cell is stimulated, the bipolar cell receiving input from it shows an immediate burst of response. A fraction of a second later, the bipolar's response rate decreases, even though the stimulation from the receptor cell remains constant. How can you account for that decrease? (*Hint*: What does the horizontal cell do?)

The receptors excite the bipolar cells. They also excite the horizontal cells, which in turn inhibit the bipolar cells. Because the route through the horizontal cells has one more synapse, it is slower than the direct route from receptors to bipolars. Therefore, the excitation arrives first and is later partly diminished by the inhibition via horizontal cells.

3. A rabbit has eyes on the sides of its head instead of in front. Would you expect rabbits to have many cells with binocular receptive fields--that is, cells that respond to both eyes? Why or why not?

Few of the cells in a rabbit's visual cortex have binocular receptive fields. A cell with a binocular receptive field becomes responsive to receptors in the two retinas that focus on the same point in the visual field. With eyes on the side of the head, few receptors in one eye have receptive fields overlapping those of a receptor in the other eye.

4. Would you expect the cortical cells of a rabbit to be just as sensitive to the effects of experience as are the cells of cats and primates? Why or why not?

One of the main features sensitive to the effects of visual experience is the response to binocular input. Given that few neurons in a rabbit respond to binocular input, visual experience probably produces fewer effects in rabbits than in cats or primates.

CHAPTER 7

THE OTHER SENSORY SYSTEMS

Chapter Outline

I. Audition

    A. Sound and the Ear

      1. Sound waves are periodic compressions of air, water, or other media.

      2. Physical and Psychological Dimensions of Sound

         a. Sound waves vary in amplitude and frequency.

         b. **Amplitude**: Intensity of a sound wave. **Loudness** is the perception of intensity.

         c. **Frequency**: Number of compressions per second, measured in hertz (Hz) of a sound.

         d. **Pitch**: Perception closely related to frequency (the higher the frequency of a sound, the higher its pitch).

         e. Most adult humans can hear vibrations from 15 to just less than 20,000 Hz.

      3. Structures of the Ear

         a. The anatomy of the ear is described in terms of three regions: the outer ear, the middle ear, and the inner ear.

         b. The outer ear includes the **pinna** (structure of flesh and cartilage attached to the side of the ear) and the auditory canal. The pinna helps us locate the source of a sound by altering reflections of sound waves.

         c. The middle ear is comprised of the **tympanic membrane** (eardrum) which vibrates at the same frequency as sound waves which strike it. Sounds wave reach the tympanic membrane through the **auditory canal**. The tympanic membrane is attached to three tiny bones (hammer, anvil, and stirrup).

         d. The inner ear consists of the **oval window**, which receives vibrations from the tiny bones of the middle ear and the **cochlea**, which contains three fluid-filled tunnels: the scala vestibuli, scala media, and scala tympani.

         e. The stirrup causes the oval window to vibrate, setting in motion all the fluid in the cochlea.

         f. The auditory receptors (**hair cells**) lie between the **basilar membrane** and the **tectorial membrane** in the cochlea.

         g. When fluid in the cochlea vibrates, a shearing action occurs which stimulates hair cells; these cells then stimulate the auditory nerve cells (eighth cranial nerve).

    B. Pitch Perception.

      1. Frequency Theory and Place Theory

      2. **Frequency Theory**: We perceive certain pitches when the basilar membrane vibrates in synchrony with a sound, causing the axons of the auditory nerve to produce action potentials at the same frequency.

      3. **Place Theory**: Each area along the basilar membrane is tuned to a specific frequency and vibrates whenever that frequency is present. Each frequency

activates hair cells at only one place along the basilar membrane and the brain distinguishes frequencies by which neurons are activated.

4. The current prevalent theory combines modifications of both frequency and place theories.

5. For low frequency sounds (below 100 Hz), the basilar membrane does vibrate in synchrony with the sound wave in accordance with frequency theory. The pitch of the sound is identified by the frequency of impulses and the loudness by the number of firing cells.

6. **Volley Principle** of pitch discrimination: Sound waves produce a volley of impulses by auditory nerve fibers, which in turn signal high frequencies to the brain.

7. For middle frequency sounds (100 to 5000 Hz), the volley principle is important for pitch perception.

8. For high frequency sounds (above 5000 Hz) we use a mechanism similar to place theory. High frequency vibrations strike the basilar membrane causing a traveling wave. This causes displacement of hair cells near the base (where the stirrup meets the cochlea). Low frequency sounds produce displacement farther along the membrane.

C. Pitch Perception in the Cerebral Cortex:
   1. Auditory information passes through several subcortical structures with an important crossover in the midbrain that enables each hemisphere of the forebrain to get its major auditory input from the opposite ear.

   2. **Primary auditory cortex**: Ultimate destination of auditory information is located in the temporal lobe within groups of cells that respond selectively to the location of sound.

   3. In another part of the primary auditory cortex cells responds selectively to tones. Cells preferring a given tone in the auditory cortex cluster together providing a map of the sounds referred to as a *tonotopic map*. Thus, the cortical area with the greatest response indicates what sound or sounds are heard.

   4. Damage to the primary auditory cortex leads to deficits in processing auditory information as opposed to a loss of hearing.

D. Hearing Loss
   1. **Conductive deafness (middle-ear deafness)**: Failure of the bones of the middle ear to transmit sound waves properly to the cochlea. This deafness can be corrected by surgery or hearing aids.

   2. **Nerve deafness (inner-ear deafness)**: Damage to the cochlea, hair cells or auditory nerve causing a permanent impairment in hearing in one to all ranges of frequencies. Nerve deafness can be inherited or caused by prenatal problems and early childhood disorders.

   3. **Tinnitus**: Frequent or constant ringing in the ear. Tinnitus is common in people with nerve deafness and is due, in some cases, to a phenomenon like phantom limb.

E. Localization of Sounds
   1. Humans localize low frequency sounds by differences in phase. We localize high frequencies by loudness differences. We can localize a sound of any frequency by its time of onset, if the onset is sudden enough.

II. The Mechanical Senses

A. The mechanical senses include touch, pain, and other body sensations as well as vestibular sensation (specialized to detect the position and movement of the head).

B. Vestibular Sensation:
1. The **vestibular organ** monitors head movements and directs compensatory movements of the eyes.
2. The vestibular organ is comprised of two *otolith organs* (the *saccule* and *utricle*) and three semicircular canals.
3. Calcium carbonate particles (otoliths) lie next to hair cells in the otolith organs and excite them when the head tilts in different directions.
4. The three **semicircular canals** are filled with a jelly like substance and are lined with hair cells. Acceleration of the head causes this substance to push against hair cells, which in turn causes action potentials from the vestibular system to travel via part of the eighth cranial nerve to the brainstem and cerebellum.

C. Somatosensation
1. The somatosensory system involves the sensation of the body and its movements, including discriminative touch, deep pressure, cold, warmth, pain, itch, tickle, and the position and movements of joints.
2. Examples of touch receptors are pain receptors, Ruffin endings, Meissner's corpuscles, and Pacinian corpuscles.
3. Stimulation of touch receptors opens sodium channels in the axon possibly starting an action potential if the stimulation is strong enough.
4. **Pacinian corpuscles** detect sudden displacements or high-frequency vibrations on the skin.
5. Receptors for heat and cold can be stimulated by certain chemicals as well as mechanical stimulation.
6. Input to the Spinal Cord and the Brain
   a. Somatosensory information from the head enters the CNS through the cranial nerves. Information from touch receptors below the head enters the spinal cord through the 31 spinal nerves and passes toward the brain.
   b. Each spinal nerve has a sensory component and a motor component. Each sensory spinal nerve innervates a limited area of the body called a dermatome.
   c. Sensory information from the spinal cord is sent to the thalamus before traveling to the somatosensory cortex in the parietal lobe.
   d. The somatosensory cortex receives information primarily from the contralateral side of the body.

D. Pain
1. Neurotransmitters of Pain
   a. Axons responsible for pain release two neurotransmitters. Mild pain releases glutamate while stronger pains releases glutamate and **Substance P**.
   b. **Opioid Mechanisms**: Systems that are responsive to opiate drugs and similar chemicals. This system is used by the body to stop prolonged pain.
   c. When activated, opiate receptors block substance P.

     d.   Opiate receptors in the brain bind to endorphins (endogenous morphines) such as met-enkephalin, leu-enkephalin, and β-endorphin. Endorphin activity inhibits pain.

     e.   **Gate Theory**: Information not related to pain travels to the spinal cord and closes the "gates" for each pain message.

     f.   Pain gates are closed by stimuli through the activation of neurons that release endorphins in the **periaqueductal gray area** and surrounding areas in the midbrain.

     g.   Endorphins block release of substance P in the spinal cord and brainstem.

2. Painful Heat

     a.   Burns are detected by special heat receptors that are also stimulated by acids.

     b.   **Capsaicin**: A chemical that stimulates heat receptors that is found in hot peppers and jalapeños.

     c.   Capsaicin also causes neurons to release substance P suddenly. This chemical eventually leads to insensitivity to pain, because neurons release substance P faster than they can resynthesize it.

     d.   High doses of capsaicin can damage pain receptors.

3. Pain and Emotion

     a.   Pain is a sensation but how much it *hurts* is an emotional reaction.

     b.   **Placebo**: a drug or other procedure with no pharmacological effects. Placebos can sometime relieve pain or at least subjective distress.

     c.   Pain activates both the sensory pathway to the somatosensory cortex and a pathway to the hypothalamus, amygdala, and cingulate cortex—areas important for emotional responses.

4. Sensitization of Pain

     a.   The body also has mechanisms to increase pain after tissue has been damaged and inflamed.

     b.   Pain sensitization is a result of the body releasing histamine, nerve growth factor, and other chemicals that are necessary to repair the body.

     c.   These chemicals also increase the number of sodium gates in nearby receptors which magnifies the pain response and they facilitate activity at capsaicin receptors.

     d.   Nonsteroidal anti-inflammatory drugs decrease pain by reducing the release of chemicals from damaged tissue. In animal experiments, the neurotrophin GDNF has been shown to have even greater pain relieving potential.

5. Pain Control

     a.   Morphine and other opiates are the primary drugs for controlling serious pain.

     b.   Morphine is most effective at relieving post surgical pain if it is taken before surgery begins, so pain messages are not allowed to increase the sensitivity of pain nerves and receptors.

     c.   A consequence of morphine use is addiction, however, morphine taken under hospital conditions almost never becomes addictive.

     d.   Morphine is better at blocking pain messages carried by thin, unmyelinated axons (dull pain) as opposed to messages carried by large-diameter axons (sharp pain).

6. Itch

a. The receptors responsible for itch have not been identified, however the sensation of itch is produced by the release of histamines.
b. The sensation of itch is transmitted much slower than the sensation of touch.
c. Itch is useful because it directs you to scratch the itchy area and remove whatever is irritating your skin.
d. Vigorous scratching produces mild pain and pain inhibits itch. Opiates reduce pain and increase itch. The inhibitory relationship between pain and itch is evidence that itch is not a type of pain.

III. The Chemical Senses

A. General Issues about Chemical Coding
1. **Labeled-line principle**: Receptors of a sensory system that respond to a limited range of stimuli and send a direct line to the brain.
2. **Across-fiber pattern principle**: Receptors of a sensory system respond to a wide range of stimuli and contributes to the perception of each of them.
3. Vertebrate sensory systems probably do not have any pure labeled-line codes. However, for the chemical senses (i.e., taste and smell) our understanding of the mechanisms used is limited.
B. Taste
1. **Taste**: The stimulation of taste buds. Taste differs from flavor which is the combination of taste and smell.
2. Taste Receptors
a. Taste receptors are actually modified skin cells which last only about 10-14 days before being replaced.
b. Mammalian taste receptors are located in taste buds, located in **papillae** (structures on the surface of the tongue). A given papillae may contain from 0 to 10 taste buds and each taste bud contains about 50 receptor cells.
c. In adult humans, taste buds are located mainly on the outside edge of the tongue.
3. How Many Kinds of Taste Receptors?
a. We have long known of the existence of at least four types of "primary" tastes: sweet, sour, salty, and bitter.
b. **Adaptation**: Decreased response to a stimulus as a result of recent exposure to it (e.g., After soaking the tongue in two sour solutions one after the other, the second solution will not taste as sour as the first).
c. **Cross-adaptation**: A reduced response to one taste because of exposure to another. There is little cross-adaptation in taste.
d. *Umami*: A taste associated with glutamate. Researchers have found the receptor responsible for this fifth type of taste.
4. Mechanisms of Taste Receptors
a. Saltiness receptors work by allowing salt to cross its membrane. The higher the concentration of salt the greater the response of the receptors (i.e., the larger the receptor potential).

          b.   Sour taste receptors close potassium channels, preventing potassium from leaving the cell when acids bind to them. The accumulation of potassium ions depolarizes the membrane.

          c.   Sweetness, bitterness, and umami receptors work by activating a G-protein that releases a second messenger within the cell.

          d.   To identify the wide range of chemicals that have a bitter taste, we have not one bitter receptor but a family of 40 to 80 bitter receptors.

   5.   Taste Coding in the Brain

          a.   The perception of taste depends on a pattern of responses across taste fibers.

          b.   Taste information from the anterior two-thirds of the tongue travels to the brain via the chorda tympani, a branch of the seventh cranial nerve (facial nerve). Information from the posterior tongue and throat is carried to the brain along branches of the ninth and tenth cranial nerves.

          c.   These three nerves project to the nucleus of the **tractus solitarius** (NTS) in the medulla. The NTS relays information to the pons, lateral hypothalamus, amygdala, thalamus, and two areas of the cerebral cortex (one responsible for taste, the insula, and the other for the sense of touch on the tongue, somatosensory cortex).

          d.   Each hemisphere of the cortex receives input mostly from the ipsilateral side of the tongue.

   6.   Individual Differences in Taste

          a.   Phenythiocarbomide (PTC) is a chemical whose taste is controlled by a single dominant gene. Some people hardly taste PTC, others taste it as bitter, and some taste it as extremely bitter.

          b.   The prevalence of nontasters of PTC varies across cultures and is not obviously related to spiciness of traditional cuisine in those cultures.

          c.   People who are insensitive to the taste of PTC are less sensitive to other tastes as well.

          d.   People who taste PTC as extremely bitter are **supertasters** and have the highest sensitivity to all tastes.

          e.   Supertasters have the largest number of *fungiform papillae* (the type of papillae near the tip of the tongue).

C. Olfaction

   1.   **Olfaction**, the sense of smell, is the detection and recognition of chemicals that come in contact with membranes inside the nose.

   2.   Olfactory Receptors

          a.   **Olfactory cells**: Neurons which line the olfactory epithelium and are responsible for smell. Each olfactory cell has cilia (threadlike dendrites) where receptor sites are located.

          b.   Olfactory cells survive for a little over a month and then are replaced by a new cell that has the same odor sensitivities as the original.

          c.   Continued stimulation of an olfactory receptor produces rapid adaptation.

          d.   Axons of olfactory receptors carry information to the olfactory bulb. Each odorous chemical excites only a limited part of the olfactory bulb. Olfaction is coded in terms of which area of the olfactory bulb is excited.

      e.   The olfactory bulb sends its axons to several parts of the cortex and the connections are precise, as all receptors sensitive to a given group of chemicals send information to the same small cluster of cells in the cortex. The organization of the olfactory cortex is almost identical from one individual to another.

      f.   From the cortex, information is sent to other areas that control feeding and reproduction.

  3. Behavioral Methods Of Identifying Olfactory Receptors

      a.   **Anosmia**: A general lack of olfaction (a **specific anosmia** is the inability to smell a specific chemical).

      b.   People with specific anosmias are used to determine how many kinds of olfactory receptors we have.

  4. Biochemical Identification of Receptor Types

      a.   Olfactory receptors are made up of a family of proteins which traverse the cell membrane seven times and respond to chemicals outside the cell by causing changes in a G-protein inside the cell. The G-protein provokes chemical activities that lead to an action potential.

      b.   Each olfactory cell expresses only one receptor gene so it is excited by a narrow range of chemicals.

      c.   It is estimated that humans have hundreds of different types of olfactory receptor proteins. Rats and mice are believed to have a thousand types.

  5. Implication for Coding

      a.   In the olfaction system the response of one receptor can identify the approximate nature of the molecule and the response of a larger population of receptors enables more precise recognition. This is possible because of the large number of olfactory receptors.

D. Vomeronasal Sensation and Pheromones

  1. The **vomeronasal organ (VNO)**: A set of receptors located near, but separate from the olfactory receptors. VNO receptors cross the membrane seven times like olfactory receptors, but there are relatively few VNO receptors (only 12 types in mice). VNO receptors also have a different structure than olfactory receptors.

  2. **Pheromones**: Chemicals released by an animal that affect the behavior of other members of the same species, especially sexually.

  3. The receptor in the VNO are specialized to respond only to pheromones. Each VNO receptor responds to just one pheromone and does not show adaptation after continued exposure.

  4. Unlike most mammals, the VNO is small in adult humans. Moreover, no receptors have been found in the human VNO.

  5. Humans do respond to pheromones and have at least one type of pheromone receptor located in the olfactory mucosa.

  6. Pheromones play a role in human sexual behavior similar to that in other mammals. Pheromones can synchronize the menstrual cycles of women who spend a lot of time together and enhance the regularity of the menstrual cycle of a women who is in an intimate relationship with a man.

IV. Attention

A. Attention is a little understood ability that can be both automatic and deliberate. It is important to study because it is central to perception and consciousness.

B. Conscious and Unconscious, Attended and Unattended Experience
   1. Subliminal (unconscious) messages do not cause an irresistible urge to obey but they can exert subtle and demonstrable effects.
   2. Several studies have demonstrated that information can enter the nervous system and slightly influence behavior even when it does not gain your attention.
   3. Studies using fMRI scans have found that conscious and unconscious material activated the same areas of the occipital and temporal cortex, but conscious material activated the areas more strongly. Also, conscious material activated the prefrontal cortex and the parietal cortices.
   4. These results imply that consciousness of a stimulus depends on how strongly it arouses the brain.
   5. A clinical case finding also supports this relationship between consciousness and brain activity, as a person who went into a comma had their brain metabolism fall to less than 2/3 it normal activity. When the person recovered consciousness, brain metabolism and electrical activity recovered to normal levels, with the parietal cortex recovering soonest.

C. Neglect
   1. Neglect is the opposite of attention.
   2. Certain types of brain damage can lead to widespread neglect of sensory information.
   3. It appears that the brain has "top-down" processes (probably originating in the prefrontal cortex) that can increase activity in other brain areas and thereby increase attention to, or consciousness of, an otherwise ignored stimulus.
   4. **Spatial neglect**: a tendency to ignore the left side of the body and its surrounding, including visual, auditory, and touch stimuli.
      a. Spatial neglect is caused by damage to the right hemisphere, especially the superior temporal gyrus.
      b. Spatial neglect can be reduced by doing manipulations to increase attention to the left side, such as giving instructions to attend to the left side or having the person look left while at the same time feeling something with the left hand.

D. Attention-Deficit Hyperactivity Disorder
   1. **Attention-Deficit Hyperactivity Disorder (ADHD)**: a disorder characterized by attention deficits (distractibility), hyperactivity (fidgetiness), impulsivity, mood swings, short temper, high sensitivity to stress, and impaired ability to make and follow plans.
   2. ADHD is common in the United States with an estimated 3-10% of children and a smaller number of adults exhibiting this disorder.
   3. ADHD is identified about 2 or 3 times as often in males as in females.
   4. ADHD is difficult to study because of the reliability of the diagnosis.
   5. Measurements of ADHD Behavior
      a. People diagnosed with ADHD differ on their performance of certain behavioral measurements such as the three tasks listed below:

- **The Choice-Delay Task**: The task gives a choice between an immediate reward or a slightly larger reward later. ADHD people are more likely to choose the immediate reward.
- **The Stop Signal Task**: A task where you are required to wait for a signal and make a response such as pushing a button as soon as the signal occurs unless another signal follows the first signal which means disregard the first signal. ADHD people have a difficult time not responding to the first signal when the disregard signal is given.
- **The Attentional Blink Task**: A task where you watch a series of black letters flashed on a screen. In each set of letters, one letter is blue and another letter is designated as the probe letter may or may not follow the blue letter. The task is to name the blue letter and state whether the probe letter came after the probe letter. ADHD people usually miss the probe letter.

6. Possible Causes and Brain Differences
   a. ADHD runs in families and is believed to be highly heritable.
   b. One form of the dopamine D_4 receptor gene is slightly more common in ADHD people than others.
   c. ADHD people have brain volumes 95% of normal, with a smaller than average right prefrontal cortex. The cerebellum also tends to be smaller in ADHD people.
   d. The differences in brain size are small and inconsistent and are not useful for making a diagnosis of ADHD.

7. Treatments
   a. The most common treatment for ADHD is stimulant drugs such as methylphenidate (Ritalin) or amphetamine.
   b. These drugs increase attentiveness, improve school performance and social relationships, and decrease impulsiveness.
   c. Amphetamine and methylphenidate increase the availability of dopamine at the postsynaptic receptors.
   d. Stimulant drugs also increase attention span in normal children.
   e. The following behavioral techniques are used to supplement or substitute for stimulant drugs:
      - Reducing distraction
      - Using lists, calendars, schedules, and so forth to organize your time
      - Practicing strategies to pace yourself
      - Learning to relax

Class Activities and Demonstrations

1. Taste Blindness: This demonstration requires the use of PTC-impregnated strips of paper which can be obtained from biology supply firms such as Carolina Biological Supply Company. Paper cups filled with water plus mints or hard candy will be appreciated by your students after this exercise. As PTC is a toxic substance, it would also be advisable to have students sign consent forms before this class exercise.

   Approximately 70% of adults living in the United States experiences a bitter taste when exposed to a dilute dose of the chemical phenylthiocarbamide (PTC); however, the remaining 30% of the population experiences no taste at all when exposed to PTC at the same dosage. Many geneticists believe that PTC taste blindness is the result of a single autosomal recessive gene pair.

   Have students chew one PTC strip before removing it from their mouth and discarding it. Within a few seconds, many of the students will experience a bitter, unpleasant taste, but some will not taste anything. Give the tasters water or mints to diminish the flavor of the PTC. After this activity is over, ask the students how individual differences in tasting PTC could possibly relate to the survival of the species (homo sapiens)?

   > Source: Singer, S. (1987). Individual differences in biological bases of behavior. In V. P. Makosky, L. G. Whittemore, and A. M. Rogers (Eds). *Activities handbook for the teaching of psychology*: Vol. 2. (pp. 289-290). Washington D.C.: American Psychological Association.

2. Gender Differences in Odor Detection: Many studies have revealed that women are more sensitive in detecting odors (including those of sex hormones) than men. A class demonstration developed by Singer (1987) measures gender differences in detecting musk perfume in small dosages. A discussion on the evolutionary significance of this gender difference can help students understand how biological factors such as olfaction can influence behavior.

   > Source: Singer, S. (1987). Individual differences in biological bases of behavior. In V.P. Makosky, L.G. Whittemore, and A.M. Rogers (Eds). *Activities handbook for the teaching of psychology*: Vol. 2. (pp. 291-292). Washington D.C.: American Psychological Association.

3. Are you a supertaster? An alternative exercise on individual differences in taste abilities requires a mirror, cotton swaps, blue food coloring, and plastic reinforcement rings for a three-hole binder. Have students use a cotton swab to wipe some blue food coloring on the tip of their tongues. Next have them place the ring on their tongue. If the students are medium tasters, they will see only a few little mushrooms (fungiform papillae) inside the ring's opening. If they are supertasters, they will find more than 25 of them within the circle.

   > Source: http://www.pbs.org/saf/special.htm. This is from the interactive activities section of the Scientific American Frontiers web site.

Class Activities and Demonstrations from Selected Web Sites

Can you find the highest note? This is a set of interactive auditory illusions created in an Interactive Multimedia Intensive seminar at the Center for Electronic Art. The site is maintained by the Exploratory: The Museum of Science, Art, and Human Perception in San Francisco. The illusions illustrated are the Shepard Scale, the Tritone Paradox, and the Risset Scale. These illusions demonstrate some very interesting phenomena of pitch perception. To prepare for this exercise it may be useful to read the following article on auditory illusions, Smith, D. (2001). Pardox of musical pitch, *The Monitor on Psychology, 32*, available online at http://www.apa.org/monitor/julaug01/musicpitch.html. Have students listen to the three illusions and answer the following two questions about pitch perception. The site can be accessed at http://www.exploratorium.edu/exhibits/highest_note/welcome.html.

Question 1: What auditory pathways are important for discriminating pitch?

Question 2: Why is language of origin thought to be important in the Tritone Paradox?

Class Activities and Demonstrations from Exploring Biological Psychology CD-ROM

Puzzle

Hearing Puzzle

Drop and Drag Activity

Somesthetic Experiment

Print Supplements

Study Guide: Chapter 7

Multimedia Resources

CNN® Today Video

1. Hearing Loss, Volume 1, Segment 5 (2:04 min).
2. Taste Changes in the Elderly, Volume 1, Segment 6 (2:02 min).

VIDEOS

1. The Senses: Eyes and Ears (Films for the Humanities and Sciences, Inc., 26 min): Describes how sensory information is processed by the eyes and ears.

2. Phantom Limb Pain (The Annenberg/CPB Collection, 20 min): This module presents a vivid example of phantom limb pain and raises an important question about the origin of pain. An

action diagram is also presented to describe how pain signals are transmitted from the spinal cord to the brain. (From the series The Mind, Episode 5 "Pain and Healing")

3. The Senses: Skin Deep (Films for the Humanities and Sciences, 26 min): Covers the mechanical senses of touch, pressure, and pain, as well as the chemical sense of olfaction.

CD-ROM

Exploring Biological Psychology
    Attention Deficit Disorder (video)
    Critical Thinking (essay questions)
    Chapter Quiz (multiple choice questions)

Related Web Sites

http://psychology.wadsworth.com/kalatbiopsych8e

On-line quizzes, weblinks, and more.

http://www.cf.ac.uk/uwcc/momed/jacob/teaching/sensory/ear.html

A concise overview of the process of sound transduction. This site was created by Dr. Tim Jacob, Professor of Cell Physiology at Cardiff University.

http://www.mankato.msus.edu/dept/comdis/kuster2/welcome.html

Comprehensive guide on internet resources for communication disorders developed by Ms. Judith Kuster, Associate Professor in the Communication Disorders Department at Minnesota State University, Mankato. This website has good links to sites on the auditory system and hearing disorders.

http://www.brainwiring.com/html/attention.html

Detailed website on ADHD and other neuropsychiatric disorders. This site has many useful links to other sites on ADHD.

http://www.painfoundation.org/default.asp

Homepage of the American Pain Foundation. This site contains a wealth of information about pain and the management of pain.

http://www.painandhealth.org/

This is the homepage for the Mayday Pain Project. This site is a comprehensive index of information on the internet about the management of chronic pain.

http://www.cf.ac.uk/biosi/staff/jacob/teaching/sensory/taste.html

This is another site created by Dr. Jacob. On this page, you will find a very good review of taste with lots of colorful graphics.

http://www.csa.com/crw/home.html

The chemoreception web page covers the sensory and biological aspects of taste, smell, pheromones, perfumes, fragrances, soaps, cosmetics, essential oils, foods, flavorings, aromas, spices, and much more. This site has wonderful links for taste and smell.

InfoTrac Key Terms for Class Discussion or Papers

1. **Tinnitus:** The sensation of noises in one or both ears. After students learn how the auditory system works have them research how different problems in this system can lead to tinnitus.

2. **Absolute Pitch:** The ability to identify or sing any note heard. Have students discuss how the auditory system contributes to this type of ability.

3. **Vertigo:** The sensation of irregular or whirling motion, either in oneself or of external objects. Have students research this dysfunction of the vestibular system.

4. **Intractable Pain:** Intractable pain is often thought to be caused by faulty processing of sensory information in the cortex. Have students research the current finding on the causes of intractable pain and the latest treatments.

5. **Aroma Therapy:** This technique is purported in the popular press to ease any number of ailments. Have students discuss what scientific evidence exists for the usefulness of this treatment.

6. **ADHD and Adults:** It is now believed that many adults suffer from ADHD. Have students read about how ADHD in adults compares to the disorder seen in children.

Critical Thinking Exercises

Cochlear Implants

Cochlear implants remain a controversial treatment for people suffering from nerve deafness. Many deaf advocates believe that the treatment is an affront to the deaf community. Have students research how the implants work to restore hearing and why some in the deaf community would be against this treatment.

Subliminal Thoughts

Science has debunked the claims that subliminal messages can create an irresistible urge to engage in a particular behavior. However, there are numerous self-help tapes sold with the premise of changing behavior through subliminal perception. Have students investigate how these tapes are supposed to work and discuss the research that would refute or support these claims.

Author's Answers to Thought Questions

1. Why do you suppose that the human auditory system evolved sensitivity to sounds in the range of 20 to 20,000 Hz instead of some other range of frequencies?

   There are two likely reasons. First, a high proportion of the important sounds on Earth are in that range. Second, sounds in that range are easy for humans to localize. Animals with smaller heads than humans have tend to hear higher pitches; animals with larger heads (such as elephants) tend to hear lower pitches.

2. The text explains how we might distinguish loudness for low-frequency sounds. How might we distinguish loudness for a high-frequency tone?

   At high pitches we distinguish pitch according to which set of neurons along the basilar membrane is most active. It is likely that we discriminate loudness of these high-pitched tones in terms of the frequency of action potentials per second by the most active set of neurons.

3. The medial part of the superior olive (a structure in the medulla) is critical for sound localization based on phase differences. The lateral part of the superior olive is critical for localization based on loudness. Which part of the superior olive would you expect to be better developed in mice? In elephants?

   Mammals with small heads, such as mice, localize sounds by loudness and therefore have a better developed lateral superior olive. Mammals with large heads, such as elephants, localize sounds by phase differences and therefore have a better developed medial superior olive.

4. Why is the vestibular sense generally useless under conditions of weightlessness?

   The vestibular sense detects the direction of head tilt by which hair cells are stimulated by the otoliths. Under conditons of weightlessness, the otoliths are not pulled in any one direction more than any other.

5. In the English language, the letter "t" has no meaning out of context; its meaning depends on its relationship to other letters. Indeed, even a word, such as *to*, has little meaning except in its connection to other words. So is language a labeled line system or an across-fiber pattern system?

   The fact that each item changes meaning depending on its context makes language analogous to an across-fiber pattern system.

6. Suppose a chemist synthesizes a new chemical, which turns out to have an odor. Presumably we do not have a specialized receptor for that chemical: explain how our receptors detect it.

That chemical must partially stimulate a number of other receptors that detect chemicals similar to this one. Every receptor responds somewhat to a whole family of chemicals (though not equally). And every chemical excites a combination of receptors. The overall experience comes from the pattern of responses across several receptors.

7. ADHD is diagnosed far more commonly in the United States today than in the past, and far more in the United States than in Europe. What possible explanations can you propose? Are any of them testable?

One possibility is that the diagnosis has simply become more popular, and more easily given, in the United States today than in other countries today or the U.S. in past times. To test the hypothesis about different diagnostic standards across countries, we could send American psychologists to, say, a French classroom and French psychologists to an American classroom, and ask them to identify probable cases of ADHD. Or ask both sets of psychologists to watch a videotape of a few classrooms and identify probable cases. The hypothesis about changes in diagnosis over time is harder to test, unless we could find a film of an American classroom from a previous era with a known number of ADHD diagnoses (perhaps zero). We could then ask contemporary psychologists to watch it and identify possible cases. The prediction is that current U.S. psychologists will identify more cases than current psychologists from other countries, and more than U.S. psychologists from a previous era did. Another hypothesis is that the actual prevalence of ADHD has increased because of increased exposure to some toxic substance, either for the children themselves or their mothers during pregnancy. If we can narrow the hypothesis to a particular toxin, we could compare ADHD frequencies in geographic areas known to differ with regard to the presence of that toxin.

CHAPTER 8

MOVEMENT

Chapter Outline

I. **The Control of Movement**

A. Muscles and Their Movements
1. All animal movement depends on the contractions of muscles. Vertebrate muscles fall into three categories:
a. **Smooth muscles**: Control movements of internal organs.
b. **Skeletal** or **striated** muscles: Control movements of body in relationship to the environment.
c. **Cardiac muscles** : Controls heart muscles and has properties intermediate between those of smooth and skeletal muscles.
2. Each muscle is composed of many individual fibers and a given axon may innervate more than one muscle fiber.
3. **Neuromuscular junction**: A synapse between a motor neuron axon and muscle fiber.
a. In skeletal muscles, acetylcholine (ACh) is released at all axons terminals at the neuromuscular junction.
4. Each muscle can contract in only one direction. In the absence of excitation it relaxes.
5. **Antagonistic muscles**: Are necessary for moving limbs in opposite directions.
a. **Flexor** muscles allow limbs to be flexed or raised.
b. **Extensor** muscles extend or straighten limbs.
6. **Myasthenia gravis**: An *autoimmune disease* (a disease in which the immune system forms antibodies that attack the individual's own body). In myasthenia gravis the immune system attacks acetylcholine receptors.
a. Symptoms include progressive weakness and rapid fatigue of skeletal muscles.
b. Treatment includes immune system suppressants and drugs that inhibit acetylcholinestrase (enzyme which breaks down ACh at the synapse).
7. Fast and Slow Muscles
a. Fish are able to swim fast regardless of the water temperature because they use more muscles in cold water and fewer muscles in warmer water.
b. Fish have three kinds of muscles:
• Red muscles: Produce slow movements almost always without fatigue.
• White muscles: Produce fast movements but fatigue quickly.
• Pink muscles: Produce responses intermediate between the red muscles and white muscles.
c. Humans have muscle fibers which are mixed together. **Fast-twitch fibers** produce fast contractions but fatigue rapidly; **slow-twitch fibers** produce less vigorous contractions without fatiguing.
d. Slow twitch fibers do not fatigue because they are **aerobic**—they use air (oxygen) during their movements.

      e.   Fast-twitch fibers fatigue after vigorous use, because the process in **anaerobic**—the process does not require oxygen. Anaerobic muscles produce lactate and phosphate which gives the sensation of muscle fatigue.

      f.   In goldfish, anaerobic muscles produce ethanol instead of lactate. The ethanol diffuses away and the muscles do not fatigue.

      g.   Humans have varying amounts of fast-twitch and slow-twitch muscle fibers and can increase one type or the other depending on which ones they use.

    8. Muscle Control by Proprioceptors

      a.   **Proprioceptor**: A receptor that detects the position or movement of a part of the body. Muscle proprioceptors detect the stretch and tension of a muscle.

      b.   **Stretch reflex**: After a muscle is stretched, the spinal cord sends a signal to contract the muscle.

      c.   **Muscle spindle**: A kind of proprioceptor. When stretched, its sensory nerve sends a message to a motor neuron in the spinal cord, which sends a message back to the muscles surrounding the spindle, causing a contraction.

      d.   **Golgi tendon organ**: Located in the tendons at opposite ends of muscles, these proprioceptors inhibit muscle contraction when it is too intense.

B. Units of Movement

    1. Voluntary and Involuntary Movements

      a.   **Reflexes**: Consistent automatic responses to stimuli which are generally thought to be *involuntary* because they are not affected by reinforcements, punishments, and motivations.

      b.   Humans have very few reflexes, although infants have several not seen in adults.

         •   **Grasp reflex**: infant reflex where placing an object in an infant's hand will cause the infant to grasp the object tightly.

         •   **Babinski reflex**: infant reflex where infant will reflexively extend the big toe and fan the others if the sole of the foot is stroked.

         •   **Rooting Reflex**: infant reflex where touching the check of an infant will cause the infant to turn its head toward the stimulated cheek and start to suck. This is actually not a pure reflex because its intensity increases when the infant is hungry.

      c.   Infant reflexes fade away with time, as they are suppressed by axons from the maturing brain. These reflexes sometimes reappear when the adult brain is damaged or temporarily impaired.

      d.   Infants and children also have certain *allied reflexes* (reflexes induced by the performance of another reflex).

      e.   Few behaviors can be classified as purely voluntary or involuntary (reflexive or nonreflexive).

    2. Movements with Different Sensitivity to Feedback

      a.   **Ballistic movements**: Once initiated, this movement cannot be altered or corrected (e.g., reflex).

      b.   Completely ballistic movements are rare, as most behaviors are subject to feedback correction.

    3. Sequences of Behaviors

a.   **Central pattern generators**: Neural mechanisms in the spinal cord or elsewhere that generate rhythmic patterns of motor output (e.g., wings flapping in birds, fin movements in fish, etc.).

b.   **Motor programs**: Fixed sequence of movements. Motor programs can be learned or built into the central nervous system.

II. Brain Mechanisms of Movement

A.   The Role of the Cerebral Cortex.

1.   **Primary motor cortex** (precentral gyrus of the frontal cortex): Stimulation of this area elicits movements, although it is not directly connected to the muscles.

2.   Axons from the primary motor cortex go to basal ganglia cells (which feed back to control later movements), while other motor axons go to the brainstem and spinal cord (which have the central pattern generators to control actual muscle movement).

3.   The cerebral cortex is particularly important for complex actions such as writing, and less important for coughing, sneezing, gagging, laughing, or crying.

4.   Stimulation of the motor cortex elicits complex movement patterns.

5.   The motor cortex is stimulated when we imagine movement.

6.   Areas Near the Primary Cortex

a.   **Posterior parietal cortex**: Keeps track of the position of the body relative to the enviroment. People with damage to the posterior parietal cortex have trouble converting their visual perceptions into actions.

b.   **Primary somatosensory cortex**: Sends sensory information to the primary motor cortex.

c.   **Prefrontal cortex**: Responds to sensory signals that lead to movements. Damage to this area leads to poorly planned movements.

d.   **Premotor cortex**: Active during preparations for a movement and somewhat active during the movement itself.

e.   **Supplementary motor cortex**: Most active while preparing for a rapid series of movements (e.g., pushing, pulling, and turning a knob or stick). Damage to the supplementary motor cortex impairs the ability to organize smooth sequences of activities.

7.   Connections from the brain to the spinal cord.

a.   **Dorsolateral tract**: Axons from the primary motor cortex and from the **red nucleus** of the midbrain synapse in the spinal cord. In the medulla lie the pyramids, where the dorsolateral tract crosses to the opposite (contralateral) side of the spinal cord. This tract controls movements of the distal limbs (e.g., hands, fingers, and toes).

b.   **Ventromedial tract**: Axons from the primary motor cortex , the supplementary motor cortex, and many other parts of the cortex. This tract also includes axons from the midbrain tectum, reticular formation and the **vestibular nucleus** (brain area that receive input from the vestibular nucleus). Axons from the ventromedial tract go to both sides of the spinal cord and are largely responsible for neck, shoulder, and trunk movements.

B. The Role of the Cerebellum
   1. *Cerebellum* (Latin for "little brain"): Involved in motor control and learned motor behavior; cerebellar damage may lead to deficits in rapid ballistic movements.
   2. **Saccades**: Ballistic eye movements from one fixation point to another. These movements depend on impulses from the cerebellum and the frontal cortex to the cranial nerves (patients with cerebellar damage may have difficulty following and fixating on moving objects).
   3. *Finger-to-nose test*: This ability relies on the cerebellar cortex to relay information to synapses in the interior of the cerebellum.
   4. Damage to the cerebellum produces symptoms similar to alcohol intoxication: clumsiness, slurred speech, and inaccurate eye movements.
   5. Cerebellum appears linked to habit formation, timing, certain aspects of attention, and other psychological functions, as well as motor functions.
   6. Cellular Organization
      a. The cerebellum receives input from the spinal cord, from each of our sensory systems via cranial nerve nuclei, and from the cerebral cortex. The information eventually reaches the **cerebellar cortex**, the surface of the cerebellum.
      b. Neurons in the cerebellar cortex have the following characteristics:
         • The neurons are arranged in a very precise geometrical pattern with multiple repetitions of the same unit.
         • Action potentials of **parallel fibers** (axons parallel to one another but perpendicular to Purkinje cells) excite one **Purkinje cell** (very flat cells in sequential planes) after another.
         • Purkinje cells inhibit cells in the **nuclei of the cerebellum** (clusters of cell bodies in the interior of the cerebellum) and the vestibular nuclei in the brain stem.
         • The output of Purkinje cells controls the timing of a movement, including onset and offset.
C. The Role of the Basal Ganglia
D. **The Basal Ganglia**: Comprised of a group of subcortical structures in the forebrain (including the **caudate nucleus, putamen,** and **globus pallidus**).
   1. The basal ganglia has multiple connections with the cerebral cortex and the thalamus. The caudate nucleus and the putamen are input areas and the globus pallidus is the output area.
   2. The basal ganglia is important for habit learning and the selection of movements.
   3. Obsessive-compulsive disorder (a psychiatric disorder marked by repetitive thoughts and actions that the person knows are pointless or nonsensical) is linked with increased activity in the caudate nucleus and the prefrontal cortex.

III. Disorders of Movements

A. Parkinson's Disease
   1. **Parkinson's Disease** (PD): Symptoms include rigidity, resting tremor, slow movements and difficulty initiating physical and mental activity. Parkinson's disease is also associated with cognitive deficits in memory and reasoning.

2. Parkinson's Disease strikes 1 person per 100 with an onset usually after age 50.
3. The immediate cause of PD is the gradual progressive death of neurons especially in the substantia nigra.
4. Possible Causes
    a. Current research suggest that genetics may be important for early-onset Parkinson's disease, but not for the more common form of Parkinson's that begins later in life.
    b. **MPTP**: A chemical that our bodies convert to **MPP,** which is a toxin that destroys dopamine neurons. Illegal drugs contaminated with MPTP can induce Parkinson's disease-like symptoms.
    c. Cigarette smoking and coffee drinking decreases the chances of developing Parkinson's Disease.
    d. Parkinson's disease probably results from a mixture of causes. A gene is responsible for many cases of early onset PD; exposure to toxins can increase risk; smoking and coffee drinking decrease risk. Diseases and infections are also currently believed to damage the dopamine cells in the substantia nigra.
5. L-Dopa Treatment
    a. **L-Dopa**: A precursor to dopamine. Commonly used as a treatment for Parkinson's disease.
    b. L-Dopa treatment is disappointing in several ways:
        • Effectiveness varies, with some patients receiving no benefit from this treatment, and its effectiveness is limited to the early and intermediate stages of disease.
        • It does not prevent the continued loss of dopamine containing neurons and it may contribute to the death of neurons.
        • It produces harmful side effects, especially in patients with the most severe symptoms.
6. Therapies other than L-Dopa
    a. Because of the limitations of L-Dopa therapy the following alternatives have been developed:
        • antioxidant drugs
        • direct dopamine agonists
        • glutamate antagonists
        • neurotrophins
        • apoptosis blockers
        • high-frequency electrical stimulation of the globus pallidus
        • surgical damage to the globus pallidus or parts of the thalamus
    b. Typically these alternatives are combined with L-Dopa.
    c. Research in brain transplants is also ongoing. Early studies in humans with transplanted adrenal and fetal cells suggested that this treatment was not very beneficial to patients. Additional animal research indicates that improved strategies using neurotrophins, stem cells, and cells from the fetuses of other species are beginning to show promise.

B. Huntington's Disease

   1. **Huntington's Disease** (HD), or *Huntington's chorea*: Severe neurological disorder with symptoms that include twitches, tremors, and writhing movements. HD strikes 1 person in 10,000.

   2. HD is associated with gradual, extensive brain damage, which is especially severe in the caudate nucleus, putamen, and globus pallidus, but also occurs in the cerbral cortex.

   3. Psychological symptoms include depression, memory deficits, anxiety, hallucinations, delusions, poor judgment, alcoholism, drug abuse, and sexual disorders. Sometimes the psychological symptoms precede the motor disorders.

   4. HD onset can occur at any age, but most often appears between the ages of 30 and 50. The earlier the onset the more rapid the deterioration.

   5. Heredity and Presymptomatic Testing

      a. HD is caused by an autosomal dominant gene on chromosome 4. The gene can be identified by a **presymptomatic test** (before the onset of symptoms) with almost 100% accuracy.

      b. The gene for HD codes for the protein, **huntingtin**, that is found through out the human body. In the brain, huntingtin is found within neurons and not on their membranes.

      c. The abnormal form of huntingtin interferes with several metabolic pathways and its discovery may make it possible to develop a treatment for HD.

Class Activities and Demonstrations

Infant reflexes: This demonstration is often used in developmental psychology classes; however, it can also be used to address the biological aspects of infant reflexes as well. Ask any parents or guardians in your class to bring an infant (preferably between the ages of 6-12 months) on the day before you discuss reflexes. Demonstrating the infant reflexes described in Chapter 8 is not difficult; just make sure students are close enough to the child to observe each movement. After the demonstration, ask students to describe any reflexes present during infancy which last for a lifetime (e.g., sneezing, coughing, eyeblinking, gagging, etc.). Finally, students should ponder two questions: (1) How is an immature nervous system responsible for infant reflexes, and (2) What is the relationship between brain damage and the presence of infant reflexes in adulthood?

Class Activities and Demonstrations from Selected Web Sites

Motor Processing Activity: Developed by P. Grobstein for the Summer Institute at Bryn Mawr College. The general purpose of this laboratory session is to better understand what is going on in the brain to yield movements which achieve particular objectives. Specifically, this exercise examines the role of sensory input for complex motor movements. Have students perform the motor tasks listed in the exercise and answer the following two question after each task. In addition, there are several good critical thinking assignment listed in the exercise. The directions for this exercise can be found at http://serendip.brynmawr.edu/bbl/Motorlab.html.

Question 1: Which motor pathways are involved in this movement?

Question 2: In addition to vision, which sensory systems must provide feedback for this movement to be accurate?

Print Supplements

Study Guide: Chapter 8

Multimedia Resources

CNN® Today Video

1. Help for the Parkinson's Patients, Volume 1, Segment 4 (1:48 min).

VIDEOS

1. Advancements in Neurology and Neurosurgery (Films for the Humanities and Sciences, 22 min): This videotape examines neurosurgical and pharmaceutical advances in the treatment of Parkinson's disease and multiple sclerosis.

2. Common Movement Disorders (Lippincott, Williams, and Wilkins, 90 min): Patients afflicted with Parkinson's disease, Huntington's disease, Multiple Sclerosis, and many other

disorders are presented in this videotape. Specific symptoms associated with each motor disease are demonstrated.

CD-ROM

Exploring Biological Psychology
    Major Motor Areas (animation)
    The Withdrawal Reflex (animation)
    The Crossed Extensor Reflex (animation)
    The Brain Pacemaker (video)
    Critical Thinking (essay questions)
    Chapter Quiz (multiple choice questions)

Related Web Sites

http://psychology.wadsworth.com/kalatbiopsych8e

    On-line quizzes, weblinks, and more.

http://www.albany.net/~tjc/descending-tracts.html

    Overview of motor control from the online text, Essentials Of Human Physiology (1992) written by Uwe Ackermann, Ph.D.

http://thalamus.wustl.edu/course/cerebell.html

    Overview of the basal ganglia and the cerebellum from The Washington University School of Medicine Neuroscience Tutorial site created by Diana Weedman Molavi, PhD.

http://www.parkinson.org

    The home page of the National Parkinson's Foundation, Inc. This site has a lot of information about Parkinson's disease and treatment. It also has good links to other Parkinson's disease internet sites.

http://www.hdsa.org/

    The home page of the Huntington's Disease Society of America. This site has great links for both basic and clinical information.

InfoTrac Key Terms for Class Discussion or Papers

1. **Spasticity**: Have student research this disorder of increased muscle tone.

2. **Poliomyelitis:** This once common motor disorder leads to a type of flaccid paralysis by targeting motor neurons. Have students research the cause of polio and why this paralysis is different from other types of paralyses.

3. **Ataxia:** Have students research this symptom of cerebellar dysfunction.

4. **Parkinson's Disease** (subdivision-surgery): Have students discuss the resurgence of surgical treatments for Parkinson's Disease. Have students compare the effectiveness of this type of treatment versus drug treatments.

Critical Thinking Exercises

Athletic Ability

There are huge differences in the ability of individuals to perform complex motor skills. Have students discuss how the different divisions of the motor system contribute to performing complex motor skills, such as hitting a baseball. In addition, have students consider how much of the individual variance is to genetics, plasticity due to practice, and variance in sensory abilities.

Parkinson's Disease and Aging

The loss of dopamine containing cells in Parkinson's disease is actually an extreme form of the natural loss of dopamine cells that occurs during normal aging. Have students debate whether this is an indication that the symptoms of Parkinson's disease are a natural result of growing old or whether these symptoms occur when we get older because of environmental insults. Have students discuss what type of research studies would be necessary to separate these two ideas.

Author's Answers to Thought Questions

1. Would you expect jaguars, cheetahs, and other great cats to have mostly slow-twitch, nonfatiguing muscles in their legs or mostly fast-twitch, quickly fatiguing muscles? What kinds of animals might have mostly the opposite kind of muscles?

   The great cats have mostly fast-twitch, quickly fatiguing muscles. Such muscles enable these cats to accelerate rapidly. However, if they do not catch their prey quickly, the prey will escape; members of the horse and deer families (for example) can run much longer than cats do before becoming exhausted. Slow-moving animals, such as sloths, have few fast-twitch muscles and many slow-twitch muscles.

2. Human infants are at first limited to gross movements of the trunk, arms, and legs. The ability to move one finger at a time matures gradually over more than the first year. What hypothesis would you suggest about which brain areas controlling movement mature early and which ones mature later?

The ventromedial tract of the spinal cord, which controls movements of the trunk and midline muscles, matures earlier than does the dorsolateral tract, which controls movements of peripheral muscles. Researchers have found that the corticospinal tract (the main source of the dorsolateral tract) has axons that continue to increase in both diameter and myelination throughout childhood and even into adolescence. Reference: Paus, T., Zijdenbos, A., Worsley, K., Collins, D. L., Blumenthal, J., Giedd, J. N., Rapoport, J. L., & Evans, A. C. (1999). Structural maturation of neural pathways in children and adolescents: In vivo study. *Science, 283*, 1908-1911.

3. Haloperidol is a drug that blocks dopamine synapses. What effect would haloperidol probably have in someone suffering from Parkinson's disease?

Haloperidol, which blocks activity dopamine, should aggravate the symptoms of Parkinson's disease.

4. Neurologists assert that if people lived long enough, sooner or later everyone would get Parkinson's disease. Why?

In apparently all people, dopamine-containing cells from the substantia nigra begin to deteriorate and die beginning at about age 45. For those who lose cells more rapidly or who had already lost cells earlier (because of blows to the head or exposure to toxic chemicals), the normal loss of dopamine neurons reaches the point that produces symptoms. Others would presumably also develop symptoms if they survived to 120 or so. (Hey, if I start to deteriorate after I reach the age of 120... oh, well!)

CHAPTER 9

RHYTHMS OF WAKEFULNESS AND SLEEP

Chapter Outline

I. **Rhythms of Wakefulness and Sleep**

A. Endogenous Cycles
1. **Endogenous circannual rhythm**: An internal calendar which prepares a species for annual seasonal changes.
2. **Endogenous circadian rhythm**: Internal rhythms which last about a day (e.g., wakefulness and sleepiness).
3. In humans, the circadian rhythm has a self-generated duration of about 24.2 hours.

B. Mechanisms of the Biological Clock
1. **Suprachiasmatic nucleus (SCN)**: Nucleus located above the optic chiasm in the hypothalamus. The SCN controls the rhythms for sleep and temperature.
   a. The neurons of the SCN generate impulses that follow a circadian rhythm.
2. The Biochemistry of the Circadian Rhythm
   a. In flies, the SCN regulates the circadian rhythms through the regulation of two genes, period (*per*) and timeless (*tim*). The *per* and *tim* genes code for the proteins Per and Tim, respectively. Early in the morning the concentration of both Per and Tim are low and they increase during the day. In the evening protein concentrations are high and result in sleepiness. During the night the genes stop producing the proteins.
   b. When Per and Tim levels are high they interact with a protein called Clock to induce sleepiness. When levels are low, the result is wakefulness.
   c. Light during the night inactivates the Tim protein and decreases sleepiness.
3. Melatonin
   a. **Melatonin**: A hormone released by the pineal gland, mainly at night, that increases sleepiness. Melatonin release usually starts 2 or 3 hours before bedtime.
   b. Melatonin stimulates receptors in the SCN to reset the biological clock.

C. Setting and Resetting the Biological Clock
1. **Free-running rhythm**: a rhythm that occurs when no stimuli reset or alter it.
2. **Zeitgeber**: stimulus (e.g., light) that is necessary for resetting the circadian rhythm.
3. In a study using hamsters housed living under constant light, the SCN in the right hemisphere got out of phase with the SCN in the left hemisphere causing two periods of wakefulness and two periods of sleep.
4. Jet Lag
   a. **Jet lag**: A disruption of our biological rhythms due to crossing time zones.
   b. *Phase-delay*: What happens to our circadian rhythms when we travel west, as we stay awake late and awaken the next day already partly adjusted to the new schedule.

  c. *Phase-advance*: What happens to our circadian rhythms when we travel east, as we tend to sleep and awaken earlier than usual.

  d. Recent studies have indicated that repeated adjustments of the circadian rhythm can damage the hippocampus and cause memory loss.

 5. Night shift workers often have difficulty adjusting to their wake/sleep cycle (e.g., waking up groggy, not sleeping well during the day, etc.). Working under lights comparable to noonday may help shift the circadian rhythms.

 6. How Light Resets the SCN

  a. The SCN is reset by the *retinohypothalamic path* that extends directly from the retina to the SCN.

  b. The retinal ganglion cells that reset the SCN are different from the ganglion cells that contribute to vision and have their own photopigment.

II. Stages of Sleep and Brain Mechanisms

 A. Stages of Sleep

  1. The electroencephalograph (EEG) records gross electrical potentials in an area of the brain through electrodes attached to the scalp.

  2. **Alpha waves** have a frequency of about 8-12 brain waves per second; these waves are typical of a relaxed state of consciousness.

  3. Stage 1 sleep is a stage of light sleep noted by the presence of irregular, jagged, low-voltage waves.

  4. Stage 2 sleep is characterized by **sleep spindles** (a burst of 12-14 Hz waves which last approximately 0.5 second) and **K-complexes** (sharp, high-amplitude waves followed by a smaller, positive wave).

  5. Stages 3 and 4 sleep are known as **slow-wave sleep** (SWS) which are comprised of slow, large amplitude waves.

 B. Paradoxical or REM Sleep

  1. **Paradoxical sleep**: sleep stage discovered in cats where brain is very active but muscles are completely relaxed.

  2. **Rapid eye movement (REM) sleep**: is a period of sleep characterized by repeated eye movements, fast low-voltage brain waves, plus breathing and heart rates similar to stage 1 sleep. Paradoxical sleep is synonymous with REM sleep, except that many animal species lack eye movements.

  3. **Polysomnograph**: A combination of EEG and eye-movement records.

  4. **Non-REM (NREM) sleep**: the stages of sleep other than REM.

  5. When people fall asleep, they enter stage 1 followed by stages 2, 3, and 4, in that order. About 60-90 min after going to sleep they cycle back from stage 4 through stages 3, 2, and then enter rapid eye movement (REM) sleep.

  6. After entering REM sleep, the sleep cycle sequence repeats with each complete cycle lasting 90 minutes.

  7. Early in the night, stages 3 and 4 predominate but toward morning stage 4 grows shorter and REM grows longer.

  8. REM sleep is associated with dreaming, but dreams can happen in **non-REM sleep**.

 B. Brain Mechanisms of Wakefulness and Arousal

1. Brain Structures of Arousal
   a. **Reticular formation**: A structure that extends from the medulla into the forebrain. Lesions through the reticular formation decrease arousal.
   b. **Pontomesencephalon**: A part of the reticular formation that contributes to cortical arousal. Stimulation of the pontomesencephalon awakens a sleeping individual or increases alertness in someone already awake.
   c. **Locus coerulus**: A structure in the pons that emits impulses, releasing norepinephrine, in response to meaningful events. The locus coerulus is also important for storing information.
   d. **Basal forebrain**: An area just anterior and dorsal to the hypothalamus whose axons release acetylcholine. Damage to the basal forebrain leads to decreased arousal, impaired learning, and attention and more time spent in non-REM sleep.
   e. Certain areas of the hypothalamus stimulate arousal by releasing histamine. Antihistamine drugs produce drowsiness if they cross the blood-brain barrier.
2. Getting to Sleep
   a. Decreasing the temperature of the brain and the body core and decreasing stimulation are important steps in reducing arousal.
   b. **Adenosine**: An important inhibitor of the basal forebrain arousal system. Caffeine increases arousal by inhibiting adenosine.
   c. **Prostaglandins**: Chemicals produced by the immune system that promote sleep by stimulating a cluster of neurons that inhibit the hypothalamic cells that increase arousal.
   d. Certain basal forebrain cells release GABA and promote sleepiness. The sleep-related basal forebrain cells get their input from the anterior and preoptic areas of the hypothalamus (areas important for temperature regulation).
D. Brain Function in REM Sleep
   1. The pons triggers the onset of REM sleep.
   2. **PGO (pons-geniculate-occipital) waves**: A distinctive pattern of high-amplitude electrical potentials associated with REM sleep. The waves are detected first in the pons, shortly afterward in the lateral geniculate nucleus of the thalamus, and then in the occipital cortex.
   3. The pons also relays messages to inhibit motor neurons in the spinal cord during REM sleep.
   4. REM sleep depends on both serotonin and acetylcholine activity for its onset and continuation. Stimulation of acetylcholine synapses quickly moves a sleeper into REM and serotonin interrupts or shortens REM sleep. Norepinephrine from the locus coeruleus also blocks REM sleep.
E. Abnormalities of sleep
   1. Insomnia
      a. **Insomnia**: Problems falling asleep or maintaining sleep. There are three categories of insomnia:
         - **Onset insomnia**: Trouble falling asleep.
         - **Maintenance insomnia**: Waking up frequently during the night after falling asleep.

- **Termination insomnia**: Waking up too early and can not go back to sleep.
    - b. Insomnia may be due to biological rhythm abnormalities (e.g., trying to sleep while body temperature rises) or the use of sleeping pills.
2. **Sleep Apnea**: Inability to breath during sleep; obesity is a common cause of this disorder, particularly in men. It is a possible cause of sudden infant death syndrome.
3. **Narcolepsy**: a disorder characterized by frequent unexpected periods of sleepiness during the day.
    - a. Symptoms include gradual or sudden attacks of sleepiness, occasional **cataplexy** (attack of muscle weakness while awake), sleep paralysis (inability to move while asleep), and *hypnagogic hallucination* (dream like experiences occurring at the onset of sleep).
    - b. Each of the symptoms of narcolepsy is interpreted as REM sleep intruding into wakefulness.
    - c. Overactive acetylcholine synapses and a deficiency in orexin (a peptide hormone produced in the hypothalamus) are two possible explanation for narcolepsy.
    - d. Narcolepsy is currently treated with stimulant drugs such as pemoline or methylphenidate.
4. **Periodic limb movement disorder**: Repeated involuntary movements of the legs and arms that can cause insomnia. The limb movements occur mostly during NREM sleep. This disorder is often treated with tranquilizers.
5. **REM behavior disorder**: Disorder where people move around vigorously during their REM periods apparently acting out their dreams. Likely due to the inability of the pons to inhibit spinal motor neurons.
6. Night Terrors, Sleep Talking, and Sleepwalking
    - a. **Night terrors**: An abrupt, anxious awakening from NREM sleep; this disorder is more common in children than adults.
    - b. **Sleep talking**: May occur during either REM or NREM sleep. It is common and harmless.
    - c. **Sleepwalking**: Usually occurs during stages 3 or 4 early in the night and is more common in children than adults.

III. **Why Sleep? Why REM? Why Dreams?**

   A. Functions of Sleep
1. **Repair and Restoration Theory of Sleep**: The body, especially the brain, requires sleep to repair itself after the exertions of the day.
2. **Evolutionary Theory of Sleep**: We sleep to save energy when we otherwise would be energy inefficient, such as during the night.

   B. The Functions of REM Sleep
1. Species with the most total sleep also have the highest percentage of REM sleep. Human infants spend more time in REM sleep and get more total sleep than adults. Adults who get the most sleep have the most REM sleep and adults who get the least sleep get the least amount of REM.

2. REM sleep deprivation leads to increased attempts at REM sleep.
3. REM sleep has been implicated in memory storage and as a way of getting oxygen to the corneas.

C. Biological Perspectives on Dreaming
1. **Activation-Synthesis Hypothesis**: During sleep, many brain regions become activated, so the brain creates a story to make sense of all this activity.
2. **Clinico-Anatomical Hypothesis**: Either internal or external stimulation activates parts of the parietal, occipital, and temporal cortex. No visual information overrides the stimulation and no criticism of the prefrontal cortex censors it, so it develops into hallucinatory perceptions.

Class Activities and Demonstrations

Dream Diaries. This is one of the most rewarding and enjoyable activities I have ever assigned to students. Although some students prefer discussing their own dreams amongst themselves, prepare yourself to be asked by many what the "true" meaning or interpretation of a particular dream is.

Approximately 2 weeks before the chapter on sleep and dreaming is discussed, tell your class to start keeping a dream diary. Encourage students to keep a pad of paper and pencil near their bed so they can write down any memory of a dream upon waking up. After 2 weeks of keeping the diary, tell students to break up into groups and discuss one or two of their dreams with the other group members. The other students in the group should be instructed to give an interpretation of the dream. To relate this activity to biopsychology, students should be encouraged to use the activation-synthesis model or the clinico-anatomical hypothesis to interpret the dreams.

An alternative activity would be to ask students to discuss one of their own dreams in front of the class so that you (the instructor) can give a brief analysis of the dream. Often students are too bashful or shy to participate, so I like to begin by discussing my own dreams first (which generally involve being surrounded by snakes) and ask students to try and analyze them. This often leads to interesting discussions of learned fears, symbolic meanings of dreams, and Freudian psychoanalysis.

Class Activities and Demonstrations from Selected Web Sites

Body Temperature and Reaction Time. This activity was developed by Dr. Rebecca Prosser at the University of Tennessee and is a part of the classroom activities on the Center for Biological Timing web page. In this activity, students monitor the effects of their circadian rhythms on reaction time by monitoring body temperature and playing a game of jacks over a two day period. The student should get an appreciation of the impact that biological rhythms have on their behavior. After students have collected the data on reaction time and body temperature, have them answer the questions listed below. The specific directions for this activity can be found at: http://www.cbt.virginia.edu/tutorial/CLASSACT.html

Question 1: To eliminate variance caused by differences in sleep schedules, the experimenter directs participants to maintain a regular schedule and start taking measurements at 8:00 am. How could this direction affect the results of people who normally sleep to 10:00 am or who typically arise at 5:00 am?

Question 2: Reaction time is typically greatest during the period when we are asleep. What could be done to decrease reaction time for people who work during this period.

Print Supplements

Study Guide: Chapter 9

Multimedia Resources

CNN® Today Video

1. Sleep Deprived Americans, Volume 1, Segment 9 (1:51 min).

VIDEOS

1. The Mind Awake and Asleep (The Annenberg/CPB Collection, 30 min): This program examines the nature of sleeping, dreaming, and altered states of consciousness. It also addresses how varying states of consciousness impact our behavior. (From the series Discovering Psychology, Episode 13)

2. Chronobiology: The Time of Our Lives (Films for the Humanities and Science, 58 min): Detailed program on how biological clocks work. The video addresses issues such as the evolution of biological clocks, the conflict between our biological clock and our current life styles, and how biological clocks can be reset.

3. Understanding Sleep (Films from the Humanities and Sciences, 51 min): This film gives a good overview of the importance of sleep to behavior and health. It also goes over topics such as biological clocks, circadian rhythms, dreams, and sleep disorders.

4. Wake Up America: A Sleep Alert (Films from the Humanities and Sciences, 18 min): This film also provides a good overview of sleep. In addition, it covers the possible functions of sleep, sleep disorders, and the functioning of a modern sleep laboratory.

5. Dreams: Theater of the Night (Films for the Humanities and Sciences, 28 min): Overview of theories on the function of dreaming and why they occur. The program covers dreaming from both a psychological and biological perspective.

6. Sleep Problems (Films for the Humanities and Sciences, 50 min): This program looks at sleep disorders that can kill--sleep apnea and narcolepsy--and shows how sleep laboratories are helping to diagnose and treat these problems.

CD-ROM

Exploring Biological Psychology
    Sleep Cycle (video)
    EEG (static image)
    Awake (animation)
    Stage 1 (animation)
    Stage 2 (animation)
    Stage 3 (animation)
    Stage 4 (animation)
    REM (animation)
    Critical Thinking (essay questions)

Chapter Quiz (multiple choice questions)

Related Web Sites

---

http://psychology.wadsworth.com/kalatbiopsych8e

On-line quizzes, weblinks, and more.

http://www.sleephomepages.org/sleepsyllabus/intro.html

The Basics of Sleep Behavior is a very comprehensive look at sleep and its functions. The site is part of an even more extensive site called the Sleep Home Page maintained by UCLA medical school.

http://vprweb.eservices.virginia.edu/cbtdocs/index.html

Home page of the Center for Biological Timing. This site has a lot of information on biological rhythms. It also has good links to other biological timing and sleep sites.

http://psych.ucsc.edu/dreams/

The Quantitative Study of Dreams site created by Adam Scheider and G. William Domhoff from the University of California, Santa Cruz. This is a great site if you are interested in the scientific study of dreams.

InfoTrac Key Terms for Class Discussion or Papers

---

1. **Jet Lag**: After learning how circadian rhythms control many aspects of our physiology and behavior, have students discuss how long plane trips lead to a disruption in the circadian cycles.

2. **Melatonin**: The chemical melatonin is now known to be important for regulating the sleep/wake cycle. Have students research the evidence pertaining to its usefulness in treating certain disorders of sleep.

3. **Napping**: Daytime sleeping has been purported by many industrial and organizational psychologist to be beneficial to work productivity. Have students discuss the research on whether napping increases overall alertness.

4. **Sleep Deprivation**: While the question of why we sleep is still unanswered, we are sure that not sleeping is bad for our well being. Have students research the various problems caused by sleep deprivation.

5. **Sleep and Memory**: Have students read and discuss the evidence that sleep is important for memory functions.

6. **Dreams** (subdivision-analysis): The interpretation of dreams is always an interesting topic to students. Have students research the current literature on how a scientist analyzes dreams.

Critical Thinking Exercises

The Night Shift

There is a large amount of research supporting the hypothesis that workers on the night shift have significantly more accidents and make more errors than workers on other time shifts. Have students discuss ways to improve the safety of workers on night shift. Also have students discuss schedules of work that would allow the night hours to be covered, but may be better suited for human circadian rhythms.

Developmental Perspectives on the Functions of Sleep

Infants sleep considerably more than adult humans. They also have sleep patterns that are qualitatively different from adults. Have students research the sleep patterns of infants and discuss how these developmental differenced support the Rest and Restoration and Evolutionary theories of sleep.

Author's Answers to Thought Questions

1. Is it possible for the onset of light to reset the circadian rhythms of a blind person? Explain.

   A person who became blind because of damage to the eyes or the optic nerves would not be able to reset a circadian rhythm based on any visual cues. However, someone who became blind because of damage to the lateral geniculate or the visual cortex should still reset circadian rhythms based on light, because branches of the optic nerve should still provide input to the SCN.

2. Why would evolution have enabled blind mole rats to synchronize their SCN activity to light, even though they cannot see well enough to make any use of the light?

   It is beneficial for them to be active mostly at night when visually oriented predators such as cats and hawks cannot see them. (If you can't see, you may as well be active when no one else can see, either.)

3. If you travel across several time zones to the east and want to use melatonin to help reset your circadian rhythm, at what time of day should you take it? What if you travel west?

   If you travel east, you want to phase-advance your circadian rhythm, so you should take the melatonin in the afternoon. If you travel west, you want to phase-delay your rhythm, so take melatonin in the morning.

4. When cats are deprived of REM sleep and then permitted uninterrupted sleep, the longer the period of deprivation—up to about 25 days—the greater the rebound of REM when they can sleep uninterrupted. However, REM deprivation for more than 25 days produces no additional rebound. Speculate on a possible explanation. (Hint: Consider what happens to PGO waves during REM deprivation.)

Evidently, animals maintain a tighter regulation of the number of PGO spikes than of the duration of REM sleep. During the REM deprivation period, the animal starts REM sleep briefly on many occasions, getting a few PGO spikes each time. As deprivation increases, the number of these REM starts increases. After severe deprivation, some PGO spikes also begin to emerge during wakefulness or during other sleep stages. After about 25 days of REM deprivation, the outlet of PGO spikes has become great enough to prevent the REM sleep need from accumulating any further.

5. Why would it be harder to deprive someone of just NREM sleep than just REM sleep?

People go through NREM sleep on the way to REM sleep. Thus any procedure that prevents NREM sleep would prevent REM sleep also.

CHAPTER 10

INTERNAL REGULATION

Chapter Outline

I. **Temperature Regulation**

   A. **Basal Metabolism**: Energy used to maintain a constant body temperature at rest. Even the most active people spend about half of their total energy expenditure on basal metabolism.

   B. **Homeostasis**: Biological processes which keep certain body variables within a fixed range. In mammals, temperature regulation, thirst, and hunger are *nearly* homeostatic and not *exactly* homeostatic.
      1. **Set point**: Level at which a homeostatic process maintains a variable.
      2. **Negative feedback**: Processes that reduce discrepancies from the set point.

   C. Controlling Body Temperature
      1. **Poikilothermic**: Animals with body temperatures the same as their environment
      2. **Homeothermic**: Animals with physiological mechanisms that maintain an almost constant body temperature despite variations in environmental temperature.
      3. The advantages of Constant High Body Temperature
         a. Mammals maintain a body temperature of 37°C for two reasons: 1) Because they have less efficient mechanisms for cooling than heating, thus it is important to have a body temperature warmer than the air. 2) Maintaining a high body temperature keeps the animal ready for rapid movement.
         b. Mammals may have developed even higher body temperatures except that protein become unstable at temperatures above 40°C.
         c. Reproductive cells require a somewhat cooler temperature than other body cells.
      4. Physiological Mechanisms
         a. The brain regions most critical for temperature control are the anterior hypothalamus and the preoptic area of the hypothalamus (preoptic because it is near the optic chiasm). Because of the close relationship between these areas they are often treated as one area, the **preoptic area/anterior hypothalamus (POA/AH)**.
         b. The POA/AH monitors body temperature by monitoring its own temperature and by receiving input from temperature-sensitive skin and spinal cord receptors.
         c. Physiological mechanisms of temperature control develop gradually in newborn mammals.
      5. The body temperature of fish, amphibians, and reptiles match that of their surroundings, but rarely fluctuate tremendously because these animals choose their location within the environment.   Mammals can also maintain their body temperature by behavioral means.
      6. After infection by bacteria, viruses, or fungi, the body mobilizes its *leukocytes* (white blood cells) to attack these foreign substances. Leukocytes release a protein

(interleukin-1) which causes the production of **prostaglandin E₁** and
prostaglandin E₂ (this causes cells in the preoptic area to raise body temperature).

II. Thirst

A. When your body needs water, the posterior pituitary gland releases **vasopressin**, also
known as **antidiuretic hormone (ADH)**, which enables the kidneys to reabsorb water
and secrete highly concentrated urine.

B. Osmotic Thirst

1. Thirst can be divided into two types: thirst due to eating salty foods (*osmotic thirst*)
and thirst due to a loss fluids (*hypovolemic thirst*).

2. **Osmotic pressure:** The tendency of water to flow across a semipermeable
membrane from an area of low concentration to areas of high concentration. In
cells, the membrane works as a semipermeable membrane and water, but not all
solutes, flows freely between the *extracellular fluid* (fluid outside the cell) and
intracellular fluid (fluid inside the cell).

3. **Osmotic thirst:** Occurs when certain neurons detect their own loss of water. This
loss of water happens when solute concentrations in the extracellular fluid are
higher than the concentration of solutes in the intracellular fluid causing water to be
drawn from the intracellular compartment to dilute the solutes in the extracellular
fluid.

4. **Organum Vasculosum Laminae Terminalis (OVLT):** Area located around the
third ventricle, the OVLT is most responsible for detecting osmotic pressure.

5. The **supraoptic nucleus** and **paraventricular nucleus** are brain areas located in
the hypothalamus that control the rate at which the posterior pituitary gland
releases vasopressin.

6. Neurons which control drinking are located in the lateral preoptic area of the
hypothalamus.

C. Hypovolemic Thirst

1. **Hypovolemic thirst:** Thirst based on blood volume (and therefore blood pressure)
becoming too low, so that water and nutrients cannot get to the body's cells.
During hypovolemic thirst the body needs to replenish both water and lost solutes
such as salt.

2. Specific sodium cravings (due to bleeding or excessive sweating) are caused by the
release of **aldosterone**, a hormone which causes the kidneys, salivary glands, and
sweat glands to conserve sodium and excrete more watery fluids than usual.

3. Mechanisms

a. **Baroreceptors:** Receptors attached to large veins that determine the pressure
of blood returning to the heart.

b. When blood volume decreases, the kidneys release the hormone *renin* which
splits a portion off angiotensinogen (a large protein in the blood) to form
angiotensin I which is then converted into **angiotensin II**; this hormone
constricts blood vessels in order to reverse the loss of blood volume.

c. **Subfornical organ (SFO):** Adjoining the third ventricle of the brain, neurons
in this brain area send information to the preoptic area after angiotensin
stimulates its neurons.

d. **Synergistic effect**: An effect that is more than the sum of two separate effects. Angiotensin and baroreceptors have a synergistic effect, as less angiotensin is required to stimulate thirst if baroreceptors also indicate low blood pressure.

III. Hunger

A. How the Digestive System Influences Food Selection
1. Digestion begins in the mouth, where food is broken down by enzymes in the saliva. Food then travels down the esophagus to the stomach, where hydrochloric acid and enzymes digest proteins. A round sphincter muscle (located between the stomach and the intestines) allows food to periodically enter the intestines. Food then enters the small intestine which is the main site for nutrient absorption into the bloodstream. These digested nutrients are carried by the blood to cells throughout the body which use some of the nutrients and store the excess as glycogen, protein, and fat. The large intestine absorbs water and minerals and lubricates remaining materials for excretion.
2. Many mammals lose their ability to metabolize **lactose** (sugar found in milk) after infancy due to decreased levels of the intestinal enzyme lactase. Worldwide most adult humans cannot consume large amounts of milk products.
3. **Carnivore**: An animal that eats meat.
4. **Herbivore**: An animal that eats plants.
5. **Omnivore**: An animal that eats both meat and plants.
6. Various behavioral strategies help to determine food selection, including preference for sweet taste, avoidance of bitter taste, preference for familiar foods, and **conditioned taste aversions** (learned dislike of a food based on past experience with the food).
B. How Taste and Digestion Control Hunger and Satiety
1. In **sham-feeding** experiments, everything an animal eats leaks out a tube connected to the esophagus or stomach (under these conditions, animals swallow several times as much as untreated animals during each meal). This demonstrates that taste and mouth cues are not enough to produce satiety.
2. Stomach and Intestines
    a. The **vagus nerve** (cranial nerve X) carries information to the brain regarding the stretching of stomach walls, providing a major basis for satiety.
    b. The **splanchnic nerves** convey information about the nutrient contents of the stomach, carrying impulses back and forth from the spinal cord to the digestive organs.
    c. The **duodenum** is part of the small intestine adjoining the stomach. Eaters become satiated when either the stomach or duodenum become distended. The duodenum also releases hormones to cause satiety.
    d. **Cholecystokinin (CCK)**: A hormone released by the duodenum to inhibit appetite.
3. Glucose, Insulin, and Glucagon
    a. **Insulin**: Facilitates entry of glucose in the bloodstream into the body's cells.
    b. **Glucagon**: Stimulates the liver to convert stored glycogen to glucose.

     c.   After a meal, insulin levels rise, glucose readily enters the cell, and appetite decreases. As time passes, blood glucose levels fall, and the body causes an increase in glucagon release and hunger is induced.

     d.   Chronically high insulin levels causes increased eating because blood glucose levels are low.

     e.   Diabetics eat more food than usual but lose weight because their body's cells are receiving little glucose due to poor insulin blood levels.

     f.   Obese people produce more insulin than do people of normal weight. The high levels of insulin cause more food than normal to be stored as fat and their appetite to return soon after a meal.

C.   Hypothalamus and Feeding Regulation

    1.   **Lateral hypothalamus**: A brain area important for the control of feeding. Damage to the lateral hypothalamus causes an animal to refuse food and water. In an intact animal, electrical stimulation of the lateral hypothalamus stimulates eating and food-seeking behaviors.

    2.   **Ventromedial hypothalamus**: Damage to this area leads to overeating and weight gain (after gaining weight these animals become picky eaters, as they consume bitter foods far less than normal but eat more than normal of a sweetened or normal diet).

    3.   **Paraventricular nucleus (PVN)**: If damaged, rats eat larger meals rather than more frequent meals.

D.   Satiety Chemicals and Eating Disorders

    1.   **Leptin**: Released by fat cells, this protein circulates through the blood and notifies the rest of the body about current fat supplies. Hunger decreases with high leptin levels in the bloodstream.

    2.   **Neuropeptide Y (NPY)**: A neuromodulator that inhibits the paraventricular nucleus, leading to an increase in eating. Leptin in the *arcuate nucleus* inhibits NPY release.

    3.   Several neurotransmitters and neurochemicals contribute to eating regulation. The complexity of eating regulation probably reflects the importance of eating.

    4.   Research has indicated that body weight is influenced by genetics. Genes can control body weight in many ways, including the amount of stomach distention needed to end a meal, preference for big breakfasts or big dinners, or how much we overeat in groups.

    5.   Weight loss can be extremely difficult. Techniques that are useful for losing weight include increased exercise, organized weight loss groups, and appetite suppressants such as *sibutramine* (Meridia).

    6.   Anorexia and Bulimia

     a.   **Anorexia nervosa**: Disorder characterized by eating much less than one needs. Anorexics become very thin and sometimes die.

     b.   **Bulimia nervosa**: Condition in which people alternate between dieting and overeating. Some individuals with this disorder force vomiting after meals.

     c.   People with bulimia tend to have higher than normal levels of peptide YY, a neuromodulator with effects similar to NPY. Bulimics have lower than normal levels of (CCK) and altered serotonin receptor sensitivity.

     d.   Bulimia shares many similarities with drug addiction.

Class Activities and Demonstrations

Comparing Eating Disorders with other Mental Illnesses: The Diagnostic and Statistical Manual, 4th edition (DSM-IV) includes separate categories for each mental illness, including eating disorders, substance abuse disorders, and obsessive-compulsive disorders (a type of anxiety disorder). However, these disorders have many similarities. For example, all three disorders are characterized by reoccurring thoughts about a particular stimulus or situation and repetitive, ritual-like behaviors. (In fact, physiological similarities between overeating and substance abuse appear to exist as well; the nucleus accumbens and the dopaminergic system do play a role in these behaviors. Some neuroscientists believe that by influencing these biological systems they can develop new treatments for these disorders.)

Begin this activity by writing three columns on the chalkboard. Label the first column "Eating disorders", the second "Substance abuse disorders" and the third "Obsessive-compulsive disorders". Ask students to first list the similarities of all three disorders. When that is accomplished, ask students to begin describing the differences between these disorders. Finally, discuss with your students why the American Psychiatric Association, which publishes the DSM-IV manual, distinguishes between these disorders even though many similarities do exist.

Print Supplements

Study Guide: Chapter 10

Multimedia Resources

CNN® Today Video

1. Hunger and the Brain, Volume 1, Segment 10 (1:48 min).
2. Fat Genes, Volume 1, Segment 11, (1:34 min).
3. Wasting Away, Volume 1, Segment 12, (2:58 min).

VIDEOS

1. Dying to be Thin (Insight Media, 60 min): This programs examines eating disorders from a psychological, sociological, and medical perspective. In addition, the video discusses why these disorder are so prevalent in women and girls.

2. Eating Disorders (Films for the Humanities and Sciences, 26 min): This program explores how anorexia develops and demonstrates its symptoms. Also discussed are the personality profiles of anorexic patients.

CD-ROM

Exploring Biological Psychology
    Pathways from the lateral hypothalamus (animation)
    Anorexia Patient: Susan (video)

Stress & Fat (video)
Critical Thinking (essay questions)
Chapter Quiz (multiple choice questions)

Related Web Sites

http://psychology.wadsworth.com/kalatbiopsych8e

On-line quizzes, weblinks, and more.

http://hyperphysics.phy-astr.gsu.edu/hbase/thermo/heatreg.html

This site examines temperature regulation from a biophysics perspective. Although the material is fairly technical, it provides a lot of useful information about how the body regulates temperature.

http://medstat.med.utah.edu/calendar/block4/ppt_eating2002/

This site is a presentation by Suzanne S. Stensaas, PhD, on hypothalamic control of eating and drinking. It is a well planned presentation of the important issues involved in homeostatic regulation and may be beneficial in creating lectures.

http://www.aedweb.org/

Homepage for the Academy of Eating Disorders. This site has excellent web links to information on eating disorders.

http://www.niddk.nih.gov/health/nutrit/nutrit.htm

Part of the web site of the National Institute of Diabetes & Digestion & Kidney Diseases (NIDDK). This section has a ton of information on the problems of obesity and weight loss programs.

http://www.healthlinkusa.com/379ent.htm

This site is a great resource for information on eating disorders as well as feeding regulation. This site is a part of the HealthlinkUSA site and has over eleven pages of links related to eating disorders.

InfoTrac Key Terms for Class Discussion or Papers

1. **Fever**: Have students research how and why the body induces a fever.

2. **Dehydration**: The importance of water to the physiology of the body is undeniable. Have students examine the consequences of dehydration to how the body functions.

3. **Appetite Depressants**: Several types of drugs are currently used to suppress appetite for potential weight loss. Have students examine the different classes of appetite depressants and the research assessing their effectiveness in reducing body weight.

4. **Childhood Obesity**: Obesity in childhood is now considered an epidemic. Have students discuss the prevalence of this disorder and the long-term problems associated with it.

Critical Thinking Exercises

Living in Extreme Environments

Humans have evolved the ability to exist almost anywhere in the world including areas of extreme cold and heat. Have students discuss adjustments humans have to make to live in extreme environments and what physiological and behavioral differences would you expect in people who live in extreme enviroments.

Are Sports Drinks Necessary?

Sport drinks have become very popular and many people drink them in lieu of water. Have students research the contents of these drinks and discuss if these drinks are of benefit to most people. If students determine that the drinks are not beneficial, ask if the extra calories and high salt content make these drinks a health hazard.

Author's Answers to Thought Questions

1. Speculate on why birds have higher body temperatures than mammals.

   The fact that birds' body temperature (about 41° C.) is higher than ours might mean either that birds find it easier than mammals do to raise their body temperature, or that they have more trouble cooling themselves. Another possibility is that a higher body temperature is particularly advantageous to birds because it facilitates faster flight. (Muscles contract faster at high temperatures. Speed is essential for a small bird that needs to fly to escape predation, and for predators that need speed to catch prey.)

2. An injection of concentrated sodium chloride triggers osmotic thirst, but an injection of equally concentrated glucose does not. Why not?

   Sodium does not readily cross membranes. Therefore, after an injection of sodium, the osmotic pressure is greater outside cells than within, and water tends to flow out of the cells, increasing thirst. Glucose, however, crosses into cells more readily, and an injection of glucose does not alter the relative amounts of water inside and outside cells.

3. If all the water you drank leaked out though a tube connected to the stomach, how would your drinking change?

Drinking would not continue uninterrupted. Your brain monitors the amount drunk and the amount reaching the stomach; when you have drunk "enough," you stop. However, because none of this water is reaching the cells that need it, thirst will return quickly.

4. Many women crave salt during menstruation or pregnancy. Why?

    Specific hungers for salt are often responses to sodium deficiency. During menstruation women lose salt along with blood; in pregnancy, a woman loses salt in the formation of the baby.

5. For most people, insulin levels tend to be higher during the day than at night. Use this fact to explain why people grow hungry a few hours after a daytime meal, but not so quickly at night.

    The higher insulin levels during the day cause much of the meal to be stored as fats; consequently, the nutrition available for the cells declines relatively quickly and the person becomes hungry again. At night, when insulin levels are lower and glucagon levels are higher, fuel stored in fat cells is mobilized and converted to glucose; this glucose supplies cellular needs without the need for more eating.

CHAPTER 11

REPRODUCTIVE BEHAVIORS

Chapter Outline

I. **The Effects of Sex Hormones**

    A. **Hormones**: Chemicals secreted by glands and carried by the blood to other organs whose activity they influence.

    B. **Endocrine glands**: Hormone-producing glands.

    C. Hormones are particularly useful for coordinating long-lasting changes in multiple parts of the body.

    D. Classes of hormones

        1. **Protein and Peptide hormones**: Composed of chains of amino acids. Proteins are longer chains; peptides are shorter. Insulin is an example of a protein hormone.

            a. These hormones attach to receptors on the cell membrane where they activate second messengers within the cell.

        2. **Steroid hormones** contain four carbon rings and are composed of cholesterol. Cortisol and corticosterone are types of steroid hormones. Steroid hormones exert their effects in two ways:

            a. They can bind to membrane receptors like protein or peptide hormones; or

            b. They can enter cells and attach to receptors in the cytoplasm, which then move to the nucleus of the cell where they determine gene expression.

        3. Sex hormones are a special category of steroids, they include estrogens, progesterone, and the androgens. These hormones are released primarily from the gonads although the adrenal gland also releases small amounts.

            Androgens: Testosterone and several other steroids. They are considered male hormones because their levels are higher in men than women.

            Estrogens: Estradiol and several other steroids. They are referred to as female hormones because their levels are higher in women than men.

            Sex-linked genes: Genes activated by sex hormones; these genes exert stronger effects in one sex than the other.

            Anabolic steroids: Testosterone and other androgens, and synthetic chemicals derived from them, that tend to build up muscle.

        4. Thyroid hormones: Hormones released by the thyroid gland. These hormones all contain iodine.

        5. Monoamine hormones: Monoamines such as norepinephrine and dopamine.

    E. Control of hormone release

        1. **Pituitary gland**: Called the "Master gland" because its secretions influence other glands in the body. The pituitary is composed of two distinct glands, the anterior and posterior pituitary.

        2. **Posterior pituitary gland**: Composed of neural tissue. Releases the hormones **oxytocin** and **vasopressin** (also known as antidiuretic hormone) which are both synthesized in the hypothalamus. These hormones are then released by

hypothalamic cells in the posterior pituitary which then releases the hormones into blood.

3. **Anterior pituitary gland**: Composed of glandular tissue. Synthesizes six hormones itself, although the hypothalamus controls their release through **releasing hormones**. The releasing hormones produced by the hypothalamus stimulates or inhibits the release of the six anterior pituitary hormones. The six hormones of the anterior pituitary are:

- **Adrenocorticotropic hormone (ACTH)**
- **Thyroid-stimulating hormone (TSH)**
- **Prolactin**
- **Somatotropin or growth hormone (GH)**
- **Follicle-Stimulating hormone (FSH)**
- **Luteinizing hormone (LH)**

F. Organizing Effect of Sex Hormones

1. **Organizing effects** of sex hormones occur mostly during a sensitive stage of development and determine whether the brain and body develop as male or female.

2. **Activating effects** of sex hormones are temporary and happen only while the hormone is present. Activating effect can occur at any time in life.

3. Sex Differences in the Gonads and the Hypothalamus

a. Sexual differentiation begins with the chromosomes. A female has an XX chromosome pattern and males have an XY.

b. **Gonads**: Reproductive organs. In mammals, the gonads of both males and females are identical early in prenatal development.

c. **SRY (sex region Y) gene**: A gene on the Y chromosome responsible for causing the primitive gonads in males to become testes.

d. **Testes**: Sperm-producing organs which also synthesize the *androgen* (male hormone) **testosterone**.

e. **Wolffian ducts**: Precursors of the male reproductive organs that develop into *seminal vesicles* (sac like structures that store semen) and the *vas deferens* (a duct from the testes into the penis) after testosterone exposure during prenatal development.

f. *Müllerian inhibiting hormone* (MIH): Peptide hormone that degenerates the Müllerian ducts in males.

g. Testosterone also results in the development of the penis and scrotum.

h. In genetic females (XX), primitive gonads become **ovaries** (egg-producing organs), her Wolffian ducts degenerate, and her Müllerian ducts develop and mature as long as she is not exposed to large amounts of testosterone.

i. **Müllerian ducts**: Precursor to female reproductive organs that develop into the oviduct, uterus, and upper vagina during prenatal development.

j. The **sexually dimorphic nucleus**: Part of the medial preoptic hypothalamus that is larger in the male than in the female. This area is linked to male sexual behavior.

k. The female hypothalamus differs from the male hypothalamus in that the former can generate a cyclic pattern of hormone release, whereas the latter cannot.

l.   **Sensitive period**: Time early in prenatal development during which a particular event has a long-lasting effect. For example, testosterone controls the development of external genitalia in humans during the third and fourth months of pregnancy.

m.   A mammal with low levels of all hormones in early development will develop a female anatomy; male characteristics develop with the introduction of testosterone.

n.   To masculinize the hypothalamus, testosterone is converted into estradiol inside neurons by the enzyme aromatase.

o.   **Alpha-fetoprotein**: A protein that binds with estrogen and keeps it from entering cells during the early sensitive period (this process prevents females from becoming masculinized by their own estrogen).

4.   Sex Differences in Nonreproductive Characteristics

a.   Female monkeys exposed to testosterone during their sensitive period are more aggressive and make more threatening facial gestures than those females without testosterone exposure. Human female children will also show an increased tendency toward traditionally male behaviors if exposed to androgens prenatally.

b.   Male and female brain areas differ in regions unrelated to sexual behavior, such as the area of the temporal lobe related to language and the corpus callosum, both of which are larger in females.

G.   Activating Effects of Sex Hormones

1.   Research Using Rodents

a.   Sex hormones activate sexual behavior partly by enhancing sensations. They also facilitate sexual behavior by binding to receptors in the brain and increasing neuronal activity.

b.   The medial preoptic area (MPOA), the ventromedial nucleus, and anterior hypothalamus are principal areas affected by sex hormones. Part of the anterior hypothalamus is known as the *sexually dimorphic nucleus* (SDN) because it is larger in males than females; however, the exact importance of this area is unclear.

c.   Sex hormones prime the MPOA and other areas to release dopamine.

d.   At low concentrations, dopamine stimulates D_1 and D_5 receptors which facilitate penile erection in males and sexually receptive postures in female rats. Higher concentrations of dopamine stimulate D_2 receptors which lead to orgasm.

2.   Sexual Behavior in Humans

a.   Effects on Men

- Among human males, sexual excitement is highest when testosterone levels are highest (between ages 15-25 years).

- Sexual pleasure during orgasm is due to the secretion of large amounts of oxytocin.

- Decreases in testosterone levels generally decrease sexual activity.

- **Impotence**: Inability to have an erection (this is usually not caused by low testosterone levels in the body). Impotence can be treated by increasing blood circulation in the penis and hypothalamus.

- Decreasing testosterone activity is a method used to treat sex offenders.
  b. Effects on Women
  - **Menstrual cycle**: A periodic variation in hormones and fertility over the course of approximately one month.
  - At the end of the menstrual period, the anterior pituitary releases **follicle-stimulating hormone (FSH)** that promotes the growth of a follicle in the ovary.
  - Toward the middle of the menstrual cycle, the follicle produces increasing amounts of **estradiol** (a type of estrogen); this leads to an increased release of FSH and **luteinizing hormone (LH)** from the anterior pituitary. FSH and LH cause the follicle to release an ovum. Progesterone is released from the remnant of the follicle and prepares the uterus for implantation of a fertilized ovum.
  - At the end of the menstrual cycle, the levels of LH, FSH, estradiol, and progesterone all decline. If the ovum is fertilized, the levels of estradiol and progesterone increase throughout pregnancy.
  - Birth-control pills, such as the combination pill (which contains both estrogen and progesterone) prevents the surge of FSH and LH that would release an ovum. The estrogen-progesterone combination also makes it harder for a sperm to reach the egg and for an egg to be implanted in the uterus.
  - **Periovulatory period**: Midway point of the menstrual cycle when sexual interest increases, possibly due to high estrogen levels.
  - **Premenstrual Syndrome** (*premenstrual dysphoric syndrome*): A disorder characterized by anxiety, irritability, and depression during the days just before the menstruation.
3. Nonsexual Behavior
  a. Testosterone increases aggressive behavior in many species of mammals and birds.
  b. Estrogen stimulates growth of dendritic spines in the hippocampus and prevents apoptosis. Decreased estrogen levels may increase the risk of Alzheimer's disease.
  c. Estrogen also increases production of dopamine D_2 and serotonin $5\text{-}HT_{2A}$ receptors in the nucleus accumbens, the prefrontal cortex, the olfactory cortex, and several other cortical areas. As these synapses contribute to sexual motivation and reinforcement, declines in estrogen levels may lead to decreased enjoyment.
  d. Estrogen has been linked to the ability to perform motor and cognitive skills.
H. Parental Behavior
1. An increase in oxytocin and prolactin by the day of delivery is necessary for the onset of maternal behavior in female rats.
2. Damage to the medial preoptic area impairs parental behavior in rats.
3. Later stages of maternal behavior are not dependent on hormones.
4. In male rats, testosterone levels drop after the delivery of their pups and prolactin levels increase.

II. Variations in Sexual Behavior
  A. Evolutionary Interpretations of Mating Behavior
   1. Interest in Multiple Mates
      a. Men are more likely to be interested in short-term sexual relationships with many partners.
      b. Men adopt one of two mating strategies: the one-mate strategy or the multiple-mate strategy. From an evolutionary point of view either strategy, or a combination of both, will be effective in spreading the man's genes.
      c. Women have less to gain in a multiple-mate strategy, as they can have only a limited number of pregnancies.
   2. What Men and Women Seek in a Mate
      a. Both men and women prefer a healthy, intelligent, honest, physically attractive mate.
      b. Men and women differ in additional preferred characteristics.
      c. Women prefer men with an acceptable odor and who are likely to be good providers.
      d. Men have a strong preference for a young partner.
   3. Differences in Jealousy
      a. Men tend to be more upset about wives' sexual infidelities than women about their husbands' infidelities.
      b. Women tend to more upset about emotional infidelity than sexual infidelity.
   4. Evolved or Learned: Just because a behavior has a clear advantage for survival or reproduction, and is similar across cultures, we can not conclude that it developed by evolution.
  B. Determinants of Gender Identity
   1. **Gender identity**: How we identify sexually and what we call ourselves (male or female).
   2. Intersexes
      a. If for any reason a female fetus is exposed to elevated androgen levels (e.g., an adrenal gland which produces an excess of testosterone), then partial masculinization of her external anatomy will occur. For example, the structural appearance of the clitoris may resemble a penis.
      b. **Hermaphrodites**: Individuals whose genitals do not match the normal development for their genetic sex. A true hermaphrodite has some normal testicular tissue plus ovarian tissue.
      c. **Intersexes** (*pseudohermaphrodite*): Individuals whose development is intermediate between male and female.
   3. **Androgen insensitivity (testicular feminization)**: Males with the genital appearance of a female. This abnormality is caused by the inability of androgens to bind to genes in a cell's nucleus; consequently, cells are insensitive to androgens and the external genitals develop similar to those of a female.
   4. *5α-reductase 2 deficiency*: Genetic disorder in males where the penis does not develop until puberty and the child is usually identified as female.
  C. Possible Biological Basis of Sexual Orientation
   1. The probability of homosexuality is highest in monozygotic twins of the originally identified homosexual person, lower in dizygotic twins, and lower still in adopted

brothers and sisters. However, if genetic factors completely determined sexual orientation, all pairs of identical twins would have the same sexual orientation.

2. Animal studies suggest that low testosterone levels during pregnancy may cause male offspring to respond sexually to either male or female partners.
3. Prenatal Stress
   a. Animal studies have shown that prenatal stress decreases male sexual behaviors.
   b. *Diethylstilbestrol* (DES): Synthetic estrogen prescribed during the 1950's and early 1960's to prevent miscarriage. DES can exert masculinizing effects similar to those of testosterone and may increase homosexual or bisexual responsiveness in human females.
4. Brain Anatomy
   a. The anterior commissure and the suprachiasmatic nucleus are larger in homosexual men compared to heterosexual men.
   b. Simon LeVay examined the interstitial nucleus 3 of the anterior hypothalamus (INAH-3) in homosexual males, as well as heterosexual males and females. He concluded that the INAH-3 of homosexual males was similar in size to the INAH-3 of heterosexual females, but smaller than the INAH-3 of heterosexual males.

Class Activities and Demonstrations

Defining normal sexual behavior: Kite (1990) has developed a classroom exercise that requires students to label specific examples of sexual behavior either normal or abnormal. Students can work in groups or individually; upon completion of the exercise, you can tabulate the results on the chalkboard. Ask students if they experienced any difficulty labeling certain behaviors as normal or abnormal. What ultimately influenced their decisions?

Source: Kite, M. E. (1990). Defining normal sexual behavior: A classroom exercise. *Teaching of Psychology, 17,* 118-119.

Print Supplements

Study Guide: Chapter 11

Multimedia Resources

VIDEOS

1. Understanding Sex (Film for the Humanities and Sciences, 51 min): A multitude of issues about the sexual behavior of plants, animals, and humans. The topics covered include, hormonal effects on development, physical attraction, genetic engineering, and sexual orientation.

2. Sugar and Spice: The Facts Behind Sex Differences (Films for the Humanities and Sciences, 51 min): This program combines case histories and scientific analyses to argue for the role that hormones play in hardwiring the brain during early development. These prenatal hormonal effects are believed to cause behavioral differences between genders later in life.

3. Gender and Sexuality (Insight Media, 30 min): Overview of the different meanings of the terms sex and gender. The video examines, gender roles, gender identity and gender-role stereotypes, and sexual orientation.

4. Homosexuality (Films for the Humanities and Sciences, 26 min): This program explores the origins of human sexuality. Examining the biological, genetic, psychological, and cultural roots of sexual behavior, it seeks to determine why some people are gay and others are not, what makes people gay—or, for that matter, what determines any sexual orientation.

5. The Gay Gene (Films for the Humanities and Sciences, 30 min): The science behind the controversial genetic research into the so-called "gay gene" is the focus of this program. A geneticist explains how the study was carried out, from initial interviews with gay men and their families, to the plotting of family trees, the extraction of DNA, and the analysis of samples in the lab. The program also considers the findings of the research: that homosexuality is, in part, genetically determined. It discusses whether these findings will advance the cause of gay rights and promote tolerance and understanding in society at large.

CD-ROM

Exploring Biological Psychology
    Menstruation Cycle (animation)
    Erectile Dysfunction (video)
    Sex Dysfunction in Women (video)
    Critical Thinking (essay questions)
    Chapter Quizzes (multiple choice questions)

Related Web Sites

http://psychology.wadsworth.com/kalatbiopsych8e

On-line quizzes, weblinks, and more.

http://wsrv.clas.virginia.edu/~rjh9u/sexdev.html

Good overview of human sex organ development and discusses variation in sexual development. This site was created by Dr. Robert Huskey for his class in Human Biology.

http://members.aol.com/gaygene/index.htm

The Gay Gene a site dedicated to the discussion of the scientific, social, political, and religious implications of research into the origins of sexual identity. This site has good links to other resources on sexual orientation.

http://ethics.acusd.edu/sexual_orientation.html

This is good site for finding the latest information on theories of sexual orientation.

InfoTrac Key Terms for Class Discussion or Papers

1. **Precocious Puberty**: Have students research the causes and treatment of this hormonally induced disorder.

2. **Hermaphroditism**: In light of new information on the importance of biology on gender identity, have student research current treatment of children born with ambiguous genitalia.

3. **Castration and Sex Offenders**: Have students research the controversy of castrating sex offenders, surgically or chemically, as a form of punishment.

4. **Gay Parenting**: Have students research the effect of sexual orientation on parenting behaviors. Particularly have students examine effect of parental sexual orientation and the child's sexual identity.

Critical Thinking Exercises

Gender vs. Sexual Behaviors

Have students compile a list of behaviors that are predominately female or male and then determine if these behaviors are based on gender or sex differences. After completing the first part of the exercise students should then discuss what criteria they used to differentiate between gender and sex.

Sexual Orientation

The role of biology in sexual orientation is still unclear. Have students examine the literature on sexual orientation and discuss the evidence supporting or refuting the position that homosexuality is biologically determined. Also, ask students how the existence of bisexuals fits in with a biological based explanation of sexual orientation.

Author's Answers to Thought Questions

1. The pill RU-486 produces abortions by blocking the effects of progesterone. Explain how this process works.

   Progesterone prepares the uterus for the implantation of a fertilized ovum. Without adequate progesterone, the ovum will be discarded.

2. The presence or absence of testosterone determines whether a mammal will differentiate as a male or a female; estrogens have no effect. In birds, the story is the opposite: The presence or absence of estrogen is critical (Adkins & Adler, 1972). What problems would sex determination by estrogen create if that were the mechanism for mammals? Why do those problems not arise in birds? (Hint: Think about the difference between live birth and hatching from an egg.)

   Mammalian fetuses share a common bloodstream with the mother, and are thus exposed to her hormones. If estrogen exerted a major influence on early sexual development, both male and female fetuses would be largely guided by their mother's sex hormones instead of their own. Birds do not face this problem, because hormones in the mother's blood do not enter the egg.

3. Antipsychotic drugs, such as haloperidol and chlorpromazine, block activity at dopamine synapses. What side effects might they have on sexual behavior?

   Drugs that decrease dopamine activity decrease sexual arousal and pleasure.

4. In all human cultures, men prefer to mate with attractive young women and women prefer men who are wealthy and successful (as well as attractive, if possible). It was remarked in the text that the similarity across cultures is not sufficient evidence to demonstrate that these preferences depend on genetics. What would be good evidence?

The strongest evidence would be that the demonstration of individual differences with a genetic basis. That is, if men have a gene that encourages a preference for attractive young women, some men presumably would have a mutation in that gene, causing a different or at least decreased preference. We could examine whether monozygotic twins have a greater concordance than dizygotic twins do for their mate preferences.

5. On the average, intersexes have IQ scores in the 110 to 125 range, well above the mean for the population (Dalton, 1968; Ehrhardt & Money, 1967; Lewis, Money, & Epstein, 1968). One possible interpretation is that a hormonal pattern intermediate between male and female promotes great intellectual development. Another possibility is that intersexuality may be more common in intelligent families than in less intelligent ones or that the more intelligent families are more likely to bring their intersex children to an investigator's attention. What kind of study would be best for deciding among these hypotheses? (For one answer, see Money & Lewis, 1966.)

The most direct approach is to measure the IQs of sexually normal brothers and sisters of the hermaphrodites. For example, Money & Lewis (1966) determined that the average IQ for one group of hermaphrodites was 110, and the average for their brothers and sisters was 109. Evidently, either the condition occurs more often than chance in intelligent families, or such families are more likely to report it.

6. Recall LeVay's study of brain anatomy in heterosexual and homosexual men (p.349). Certain critics have suggested that one or more of the men classified as "heterosexual" might actually have been homosexual or bisexual. If so, would that fact strengthen or weaken the overall conclusions?

If some homosexual or bisexual men were misclassified as heterosexual, that fact would actually strengthen the conclusions. I know that sounds odd, but here's why: The more accurately an investigator classifies individuals into two groups, the greater the probability of detecting any difference that might actually exist between those groups. Therefore, an occasional inaccuracy in classification makes it harder to detect such a difference. If an investigator had some errors in classification and managed to detect a difference between the groups anyway, the true difference between the groups must be large. (This answer assumes that the errors in classification were random. The answer would be different if someone systematically misclassified some people as homosexual or heterosexual in a way that correlated with differences in brain anatomy.)

CHAPTER 12

EMOTIONAL BEHAVIORS

Chapter Outline

I. **What Is Emotion?**

  A. For research purposes, *emotions* are defined as observable behaviors as opposed to feelings which are *private experiences*.

  B. **Absence seizure**: A type of epilepsy where a person has brief periods when they stare blankly without talking or moving. During the absence seizure people have an interruption of their normal conscious state and have no emotional expressions.

  C. Strong emotions may impair reasoning, but lack of emotions can also lead to poor decision making.

  D. Emotions, Autonomic Arousal, and the James-Lange Theory

    1. **James-Lange theory**: Autonomic arousal and skeletal actions occur before an emotion. An emotion is the label we give to our physiological responses.

    2. The cognitive component of emotion does not need feedback from the rest of the body.

    3. **Pure autonomic failure**: Uncommon condition in which output from the autonomic nervous system to the body fails, either completely or almost completely. People with this disorder have no changes in autonomic response to psychological or physical stress. These people report having the same emotions as any one else although the emotions are less intense.

    4. **Locked-In Syndrome**: Caused by damage in the ventral part of the brainstem and leaves a person unable to make any voluntary movement other than moving the eyes. People with this syndrome report feeling tranquil.

    5. **Panic Disorder**: A condition marked by episodes of extreme sympathetic nervous system arousal which the person interprets as fear.

    6. Perceptions of our bodily reactions are important for interpreting our emotions. We recognize extreme arousal as extreme fear or panic, and stimuli that induce smiling or laughter are considered pleasant or amusing.

  E. Brain Areas Associated with Emotion

    1. **Limbic System**: A forebrain area, which forms a border around the brainstem, traditionally regarded as critical for emotion. Other areas identified as important for emotion include the cingulate cortex, hypothalamus, parts of the somatosensory cortex, and the midbrain.

    2. Brain areas responsible for different types of emotion have also been identified. For example, the medial frontal cortex is important for identifying angry expressions and the insular cortex is necessary for the emotional experience of *disgust*.

    3. The right hemisphere appears to be more responsive to emotional stimuli than the left. The right hemisphere is especially activated by unpleasant emotions.

II. Stress and Health

A. **Behavioral medicine**: Emphasizes effects of diet, smoking, exercise, and other behaviors on health.
B. **Stress**: The nonspecific response of the body to any demand made upon it.
C. **Psychosomatic Illness**: An illness whose onset is influenced by someone's personality, emotions, or experience.
   1. **Ulcers** are thought to arise from a combined influence of *Helicobacer pylori* (a type of bacteria), current and past stressful experiences, and drugs that irritate the digestive system wall.
   2. **Heart disease** is more common in people who are frequently hostile than among people who are relaxed and easy going.
   3. Individuals with strong social support (i.e., friends and family) tend to keep their heart rates and blood pressure low during stressful situations.
   4. **Voodoo death**: Death that is apparently due to the belief that a curse has destined death; however, death may actually be the result of a massive parasympathetic response causing the heart to stop altogether.
   5. **Serendipity**: The process of stumbling upon something interesting while looking for something less interesting. Many scientific advances, such as why people die after being cursed, have been made in this way.
D. Stress and the Hypothalamus-Pituitary-Adrenal Cortex Axis
   1. Stress activates both the autonomic nervous system and the **HPA axis**-hypothalamus, pituitary gland, and adrenal cortex. In fact, prolonged stress increasingly activates the HPA axis.
      a. Stress activates the hypothalamus which sends messages to the anterior pituitary gland to secrete adrenocorticotropic hormone (**ACTH**); this hormone stimulates the adrenal cortex to secrete **cortisol**, which increases blood sugar levels and enhances metabolism.
   2. **Immune system**: Comprised of cells which protect the body against intruders such as bacteria and viruses. An *autoimmune disease* is the result of the immune system attacking normal cells.
      a. **Leukocytes**: White blood cells which are produced in the bone marrow before migrating to the thymus gland, spleen, and peripheral lymph nodes. Leukocytes patrol the blood and other body fluids looking for intruders.
      b. **Antigens** (antibody-generator molecules): Proteins located on a cell surface. When leukocytes discover cells with antigens different from the rest of the body, they attack those cells.
      c. **Macrophages**: A cell that surrounds a bacterium or other intruder, digests it, and exposes its antigens on the macrophage's own surface.
      d. **B cells**: Leukocytes which mature in the bone marrow and produce specific antibodies to attack an antigen.
      e. **Antibodies**: Y-shaped proteins which circulate in the blood and attach specifically to one kind of antigen. The body develops antibodies against antigens that it has encountered in the past.

       f.   **T cells**: Leukocytes which mature in the thymus. T cells have two types: cytotoxic T cells which directly attack intruder cells and helper T cells which stimulate other T cells or B cells to multiply more rapidly.

       g.   **Natural killer cells**: Blood cells which attach to cells infected with viruses and certain kinds of tumor cells.

       h.   **Cytokines**: Chemicals released by the immune system which cross the blood-brain barrier and influence neuronal function.

   3. **Psychoneuroimmunology**: Deals with the ways in which experiences, especially stressful ones, alter the immune system, and how the immune system in turn influences the central nervous system.

       a.   The body handles powerful inescapable, but temporary stressors like illnesses (i.e., fever production, increase in sleep, decrease in appetite and sex drive).

       b.   Prolonged stress leads to prolonged increases in cortisol and other hormones which direct energy toward increasing blood sugar and metabolism by shifting energy away from synthesizing proteins, including immune system proteins. If stress continues for weeks or months, the immune system may weaken, leaving the individual vulnerable to many illnesses.

       c.   High cortisol levels impair memory and increase the vulnerability of neurons in the hippocampus, so that toxins or overstimulation will kill the neurons.

E. **Posttraumatic Stress Disorder (PTSD)**: Psychiatric disorder that occurs in some people who have had a traumatic experience of being severely injured or threatened or seeing other people harmed or killed.

   1. Symptoms of PTSD include frequent distressing recollections (flashbacks) and nightmares about the traumatic event, avoidance of reminders of it, and exaggerated arousal in response to noises and other stimuli.

   2. PTSD victims have a smaller than average hippocampus and have lower than normal cortisol levels.

III. Attack and Escape Behaviors

A. Attack Behaviors

   1. Attack behavior is usually triggered by some sort of pain or threat.

   2. Attack behaviors can be primed by stimulating the corticomedial area of the amygdala in hamsters. In fact, this area shows increased neural activity immediately after a first attack on an intruding hamster.

   3. Heredity and Environment in Violence

       a.   Many studies of twins and adoptees have consistently found evidence of genetic contributions to aggression, antisocial, and criminal behavior. However, these studies do not distinguish between the effects of genetics and prenatal environment.

       b.   One study found that monozygotic twins were more likely to resemble each other in adult crimes and aggressive behaviors than were dizygotic twins.

       c.   Another study found that adopted children, who had biological parents with criminal records and a troubled adoptive home, were more likely to exhibit aggressive behaviors and conduct disorders.

   4. Hormones

       a.   Among nonhuman animals, male aggressive behavior depends heavily on testosterone. In humans, men with higher levels of testosterone have, on average, slightly higher rates of violent activities and criminal behaviors than do other men.

       b.   A recent study found young women injected with testosterone showed a greater than usual increase in heart rate when they looked at a picture of angry faces. This suggests that testosterone may induce people to attend longer and respond more vigorously to certain situations.

  5. Brain Abnormalities and Violence

       a.   Testosterone exerts its effect on aggression by facilitating activity in several brain areas.

       b.   **Intermittent explosive disorder**: A condition marked by occasional outbursts of violent behavior with little or no provocation. It is sometimes linked with temporal lobe epilepsy.

       c.   People with damage to the prefrontal cortex also fight or threaten more frequently and with less provocation than other people. Prefrontal damage causes a general loss of inhibition and a tendency toward many socially inappropriate behaviors, not just violent ones.

  6. Serotonin Synapses and Aggressive Behavior.

       a.   **Turnover**: Amount of release and resynthesis of a neurotransmitter by presynaptic neurons. Serotonin turnover can be inferred by measuring the concentration of **5-hydroxyindoleacetic acid (5-HIAA)**, a serotonin metabolite.

       b.   Luigi Valzelli found that social isolation induced a drop in serotonin turnover in the brains of male mice, an effect that further increased the possibility of aggressive behavior toward other males.

       c.   In a study of 2-year-old male monkeys, researchers found that monkeys with the lowest serotonin turnover had the highest amount of aggressive behaviors. Moreover, these monkeys died before the age of 6, while monkeys with higher serotonin turnover were alive at 6.

       d.   Low serotonin turnover is not linked specifically to violence, but to a decreased inhibition of impulses.

       e.   Data from human studies suggest a lower-than-normal serotonin turnover in those convicted of violent crimes as well as those who committed or attempted a violent suicide.

       f.   Neurons synthesize serotonin from tryptophan (an amino acid found in proteins). A diet high in other amino acids, but low in tryptophan, impairs the brain's ability to synthesize serotonin. One study found an increase in aggressive behavior in young men a few hours after eating a diet low in tryptophan.

B. Escape, Fear, and Anxiety

  1. Fear, Anxiety, and the Amygdala

       a.   Fear is a temporary experience; if one escapes from danger, fear will soon subside. Anxiety is a longer-lasting, less escapable state. Many psychological disorders result in part from excess anxiety.

       b.   **Startle reflex**: Response one makes to a sudden, unexpected loud noise.

    c.   The amygdala enhances the startle reflex by sending axons to the hypothalamus (for controlling autonomic fear responses) and by relaying information to the *central gray* area in the midbrain (this area in turn sends axons to the pons, triggering the startle reflex).

    d.   *Klüver-Bucy syndrome*: Tameness and placidity in monkeys following damage or removal of the amygdala.

    e.   People suffering from *Urbach-Wiethe disease* (a genetic disorder which causes gradual atrophy of the amygdala) only weakly experience fear and related emotions. These individuals also have difficulty recognizing fear in others.

2.   Anxiety-Reducing Drugs

    a.   CCK (cholecystokinin) is one of the main excitatory neuromodulators in the amygdala. Injections of CCK-stimulating drugs into the amygdala enhance the startle reflex.

    b.   GABA (gamma amino butyric acid) is the main inhibitory neurotransmitter found in the amygdala. Injections of GABA blockers can induce outright panic.

    c.   **Barbiturates**: A widely used tranquilizer a decade ago. These drugs have been replaced by safer drugs because they can be fatal, especially if they are combined them with alcohol.

    d.   **Benzodiazepines**: Commonly used class of tranquilizers. The benzodiazepines include diazepam, chlordiazepoxide, and alprazolam. These drugs bind to a receptor site on the $GABA_A$ receptor complex which causes the receptor to change shape, allowing GABA to attach more easily and bind more tightly to it.

    e.   Benzodiazepines exert their antianxiety effects in the amygdala and hypothalamus.

    f.   **Diazepam-binding inhibitor (DBI)**: Also known as **endozepine**, this protein binds to the same sites as benzodiazepines, but blocks their behavioral effects.

    g.   Alcohol has behavioral effects similar to the benzodiazepines. A combination of alcohol and tranquilizers can be fatal. Alcohol, benzodiazepines, and barbiturates all exhibit **cross-tolerance** (a phenomenon where an individual who develops tolerance to one of the drugs will show partial tolerance to the other drugs).

Class Activities and Demonstrations

1. The Obsessive-Compulsive Test: The Diagnostic and Statistical Manual, fourth edition (DSM-IV) defines obsessions as "persistent ideas, thoughts, impulses, or images that are experienced as intrusive and inappropriate and that cause marked anxiety"; it also defines compulsions as "repetitive behaviors or mental acts the goal of which is to reduce anxiety or stress." Have students complete the test developed by R. M. Gardner (1980) and compare their results in class.

    Sources: American Psychiatric Association (1994). *Diagnostic and statistical manual of mental disorders*. Washington D.C.; Gardner, R. M. (1980) *Exercises for general psychology*. Minneapolis: Burgess.

2. The Polygraph Test: Recruit a student volunteer for a brief polygraph demonstration (many large universities have a polygraph available). Be sure to begin the demonstration by asking baseline questions (regarding name, age, occupation, etc.). Afterwards, begin asking questions of interest (some topics to consider would be past or present illicit drug use, past criminal activity, study habits, etc.). The demonstration works best if student volunteers take the subject matter seriously and try to answer sincerely.

Print Supplements

Study Guide: Chapter 12

Multimedia Resources

CNN® Today Video

1. Post-Traumatic Stress and 9/11, Volume 1, Segment 14 (2:40 min).

VIDEOS

1. Emotions and Illness (Film for the Humanities and Science, 30 min): Video talks about the negative impact of stress on health. In addition, the video addresses how effective management of stress can improve health and treatment outcome.

2. The Mind of a Killer: Case Study of a Murderer (Film for the Humanities and Science, 46 min): Profile of serial killer, Joel Rifkin. The video addresses possible biological mechanisms for his motivation to kill.

3. Circuits of Fear: Anxiety Disorders (Film for the Humanities and Science, 51 min): Presents an overview of anxiety disorders, including panic disorder, obsessive-compulsive disorder, and post-traumatic stress disorder. The video covers drug treatments, psychotherapy, and recent finding on brain circuitry using imaging technologies.

4. Health, Stress, and Coping (Insight Media, 30 min): This program explores effects of various types of stressors including daily stress, posttraumatic stress syndrome, and loss of love relationships. Case studies illuminate the link between stress and physical health.

CD-ROM

Exploring Biological Psychology
    Amygdala and Fear Conditioning (animation)
    Health and Stress (video)
    Stress and the Brain (video)
    CNS Depressants (video)
    Critical Thinking (essay questions)
    Chapter Quiz (multiple choice questions)

Related Web Sites

http://psychology.wadsworth.com/kalatbiopsych8e

On-line quizzes, weblinks, and more.

http://trochim.human.cornell.edu/gallery/young/emotion.htm#methods

This page is an on-line bibliography in the area of emotions and emotional intelligence, describing current research findings and notes of interest.

http://www.teachhealth.com/index.html

An easy to read site on the biological basis of stress, depression, anxiety, sleep problems, and drug use. It also has good links to other resources on stress.

http://www.ncptsd.org/index.html

This is the home page of the National Center for PTSD, a program of the U.S. Department of Veterans Affairs. This a very comprehensive web site on posttraumatic stress disorder with links to numerous other resources.

http://aggression.virtualave.net/aggression.html

The Aggression-Driven Depression site is created and maintained by Gert Noordhoek. This site provides information about the link between aggression, depression, and the neurotransmitter serotonin.

http://www.crime-times.org/

Crime Times is an on-line journal published quarterly by the Wacker Foundation, a non-profit organization. The journal contains research reviews and important information on the biological causes of criminal, violent, and psychopathic behavior.

InfoTrac Key Terms for Class Discussion or Papers

1. **Emotional Intelligence** (EI): EI is being defined as a group of mental abilities which help you recognize and understand your own feelings and others'. Have students discuss how scientists assess EI and the diverse ways in which this measure is being used.

2. **Psychoneuroimmunology**: This relatively new field examines the relationship between the immune system, endocrine system, and the CNS. Have students research the current finding on how stress can impair our immune systems.

3. **Stress and Memory**: Have students research how stress can impair memory functions.

4. **Panic Disorder**: Have students research current treatments for this disorder of heightened fear or anxiety.

5. **Anxiety and Antidepressants**: Many types of anxiety are regularly treated with antidepressant medications. Have students discuss the clinical research on the effectiveness of these drugs versus traditional anti-anxiety drug treatments.

Critical Thinking Exercises

Does Mr. Spock Have Emotions?

The television and movie character from the Star Trek series, Mr. Spock, was most notable for his lack of emotion. His lack of emotion was demonstrated primarily by his lack of behavioral responses to stimuli and situations that induced emotional responses from the characters surrounding him. Based on the definition of emotion discussed in the text, have students debate whether Mr. Spock truly lacked emotions. What other criteria would be necessary to make this determination?

Empathy and the Amygdala

Empathy is the ability to understand and identify with other's feelings, situations, and motives. An important aspect of empathy is the ability to correctly distinguish someone else's emotional state. Have students discuss if the amygdala is necessary for empathy. What changes in empathic abilities would you expect in someone with damage to the amygdala?

Author's Answers to Thought Questions

1. If you believe you are at risk for ulcers, and you have just had an extremely stressful experience, what might you do to decrease the risk of ulcers?

The stressful experience itself strongly stimulates much of the sympathetic nervous system. At the end of the stressful experience, a rebound increase in parasympathetic activity increases secretions by the stomach and intestines, potentially damaging the insides of those organs themselves. One good strategy would be to nibble on snacks to keep something in the digestive system to absorb digestive juices. Another possibility would be to try to calm down gradually, maintaining enough sympathetic arousal to prevent a sudden overshoot by the parasympathetic output to the stomach and intestines.

2. If someone were unable to produce cytokines, what would be the consequences?

   During illness the person would fail to experience fever, sleepiness, loss of appetite, or decreased sex drive.

3. Much of the play behavior of a cat can be analyzed into attack and escape components. Is the same true for children's play?

   (An uncharacteristically easy thought question.) Yes, much of children's play also relates to attack and escape; so does the play behavior of most other mammals. So does a fair amount of the play behavior of adult humans. Many sports and games have aspects of offense and defense.

CHAPTER 13

THE BIOLOGY OF LEARNING AND MEMORY

Chapter Outline

I. **Learning, Memory, Amnesia, and Brain Functioning**

    A. Localized Representations of Memory

        1. **Classical Conditioning**: After repeated presentations of a **conditioned stimulus (CS)**, which initially elicits no response, with an **unconditioned stimulus (UCS)**, which automatically elicits an **unconditioned response (UCR)**, the subject begins responding to the CS in a way similar to the UCS.

        2. **Operant Conditioning**: Behavior is followed by a **reinforcement** (which increases the future probability of a response) or **punishment** (which suppresses the frequency of a response).

        3. **Engram**: Physical representation of learning.

           a. Karl Lashley's work on learning after cortical lesions led him to propose two principles about the nervous system:

               • **Equipotentiality**: All parts of the cortex contribute equally to complex behaviors like learning; any part of the cortex can substitute for any other.

               • **Mass action**: The cortex works as a whole, and the more cortex the better.

        4. Karl Lashley believed that the cerebral cortex was the best place to search for an engram, but years later Richard F. Thompson located an engram of memory in the cerebellum.

           a. **Lateral interpositus nucleus (LIP)**: Damage to this area of the cerebellum leads to permanent loss of a classically conditioned eyeblink response in rabbits.

    B. Types of memory and amnesia

        1. **Short-term memory**: Memory of events that have just occurred.

        2. **Long-term memory**: Memory of events from previous times.

        3. Donald Hebb theorized that any memory that stayed in short-term storage long enough would be gradually **consolidated** (strengthened) into a long-term memory.

           a. The brain produces a chemical to interfere with consolidation called *protein phosphatase 1*. This chemical declines when the experience is repeated and allows for consolidation.

           b. Meaningful and emotional information are more likely to be consolidated than other information, because of increased stimulation to the amygdala.

        4. **Working memory**: Temporary storage of memories about a task that one is attending to at the moment. Working memory has three components:

               • **Phonological loop**: Process which stores auditory information (including words).

               • **Visuospatial scratchpad**: Stores visual information.

               • **Central executive**: Directs attention toward one stimulus or another and determines what information will be stored in working memory. The ability to shift attention between one task and another appears dependent on the prefrontal cortex.

5. **Delayed-response task**: Memory task in which a subject is given a signal to which it must give a learned response after a delay. A common test for working memory.

C. The Hippocampus and Amnesia

1. Memory Loss After Hippocampal Damage

   a. **Amnesia**: Memory loss. Damage to the hippocampus produces a powerful kind of amnesia.

   b. Patient H. M. had his hippocampus and surrounding brain tissue removed from both hemispheres in 1953 to treat his severe epilepsy. However, he suffered moderate **retrograde amnesia** (loss of memory for events that occurred shortly before brain damage) and severe **anterograde amnesia** (loss of long-term memories for events that happened after brain damage) as a result of the bilateral hippocampal removal.

   c. H. M. lost his **declarative memory** (the ability to state a memory in words), but retained his **procedural memory** (development of motor skills and responses).

   d. H. M. also has better **implicit memory** (influence of a recent experience on behavior, even if one does not realize that he or she is using memory at all) than **explicit memory** (deliberate recall of information that one recognizes as a memory).

2. Theories of the Function of the Hippocampus

   a. **Delayed matching-to-sample task**: Task used to measure declarative memory in animals. In this procedure, animals see an object (the sample) and after a delay get to choose between two objects, one of which matches the sample.

   b. **Delayed nonmatching-to-sample task**: Similar to the above task except the animal must choose the one that differs from the sample.

   c. Hippocampal damage impairs performance on both delayed matching-to-sample and delayed nonmatching-to-sample tasks.

   d. **Episodic memories**: Declarative memories of a single event.

   e. In rats, many hippocampal neurons are tuned to particular spatial locations. In human cab drivers, imaging data has shown that the hippocampus is activated when answering spatial questions and they have a larger than normal posterior hippocampus.

   f. **Radial Maze**: Maze with eight or more arms used to test spatial memory in animals. Damage to the hippocampus impairs performance on this task.

   g. **Morris search task**: Procedure where an animal has to find a hidden platform usually under murky water. This procedure is used to task spatial memory in animals and, like the radial maze, performance is negatively impacted by hippocampal damage.

   h. In certain closely related species of birds, the larger the hippocampus the better their performance on spatial memory tasks.

   i. **Configural Learning**: Procedure where the meaning of a stimulus depends on what other stimuli are paired with it. Early researchers believed that the hippocampus was necessary for this type of learning, because damage to the hippocampus impaired performance. However more recent researchers have argued that this type of task is not unique to the hippocampus. The impairment of performance after hippocampal damage is now believed to be due to the complexity of the task not the type of learning.

    j.   Damage to the hippocampus results in elevated levels of adrenal hormones. It is hypothesized by some researchers that the memory impairment is due to this increase in adrenal hormones.

D. Other Types of Brain Damage and Amnesia

  1. **Korsakoff's syndrome** or *Wernicke-Korsakoff's syndrome*: Brain damage caused by prolonged thiamine deficiency (this disorder is most commonly seen in chronic alcoholics).

    a.   Thiamine deficiency leads to brain cell loss in the mamillary bodies of the hypothalamus and the dorsomedial nucleus of the thalamus, which projects to the prefrontal cortex.

    b.   Korsakoff's patients show apathy, confusion, and have trouble reasoning about their memories. Patients with Korsakoff's syndrome also have both anterograde and retrograde amnesia.

    c.   **Priming**: Type of implicit memory. Phenomenon that seeing or hearing words temporarily increases one's probability of using them. Like H. M., people with Korsakoff's syndrome have better implicit than explicit memory.

    d.   **Confabulation**: Making up an answer to a question and accepting the invented answer as if it were true (a common symptom of Korsakoff's syndrome).

  2. Alzheimer's disease: A dementia which becomes more prevalent with advancing age. Symptoms include short-term and long-term memory loss, confusion, restlessness, hallucinations, and disturbances of eating and sleeping.

    a.   People with Alzheimer's disease have better procedural than declarative memory and better implicit than explicit memory.

    b.   People with *Down syndrome* (a type of mental retardation) usually get Alzheimer's disease if they survive into middle age.

    c.   Abnormal genes located on several different chromosomes can lead to an accumulation of *amyloid* deposits in the brain. The amyloid precursor protein is a large protein that is cleaved to form $A\beta_{40}$ in normal cells, but in Alzheimer's disease it is cleaved into a slighter larger protein **amyloid beta protein 42 ($A\beta_{42}$)**. Deposits of amyloid cause neuronal degeneration in the brain, and the dying axons and dendrites form **plaques** in many areas of the cerebral cortex and hippocampus, as well as other brain areas. The protein, *Tau,* also accumulates and produces **tangles** from the dying cell bodies.

II. Storing Information in the Nervous System

A. **Hebbian synapse**: A synapse that increases in effectiveness because of simultaneous activity in the presynaptic and postsynaptic neurons.

B. *Aplysia* as an Experimental Animal

  1. *Aplysia* is a marine invertebrate often used for physiological studies of learning. *Aplysia* have fewer neurons than any vertebrate, and many are large and easy to study. A commonly studied behavior in the Aplysia is the gill withdrawal response.

2. **Habituation**: A decrease in response to a stimulus that is presented repeatedly and is accompanied by no change in other stimuli. Habituation in *Aplysia* reflects a decrease in neurotransmission between the sensory neuron and a motor neuron.

3. **Sensitization**: An increase in response to a mild stimulus after an intense stimulus has been presented. Sensitization in *Aplysia* depends on the release of serotonin by a facilitating interneuron onto the synapses of many presynaptic sensory neurons; this process ultimately blocks potassium channels and thereby prolongs the release of transmitter from that neuron.

C. Long-Term Potentiation in Mammals

1. **Long-term potentiation (LTP)**: Increased responsiveness to axonal input as a result of a previous period of rapidly repeated stimulation. LTP has three properties that make it an attractive candidate for the cellular basis of learning and memory:

   a. **Specificity**: Only activated synapses become strengthened.

   b. **Cooperativity**: Nearly simultaneous stimulation by two or more axons produces LTP; stimulation by just one axon produces it weakly.

   c. **Associativity**: Pairing a weak input with a strong input enhances later responses to the weak input.

2. **Long-term depression (LTD)**: A prolonged decrease in responsiveness to synaptic input after repeated pairing with some previous input, that is generally of low frequency. LTD occurs in the cerebellum and hippocampus.

3. Almost all known cases of LTP depend on changes at glutamate receptors, especially the **NMDA** and **AMPA** type of glutamate receptors.

4. Usually glutamate produces neither excitatory nor inhibitory effects at NMDA receptors, because magnesium blocks ion channels located on this receptor.

5. About the only way to activate NMDA receptors is first to repeatedly stimulate nearby AMPA glutamate receptors, thereby depolarizing the dendrite. Depolarization repels the magnesium ions and allows glutamate to open NMDA channels so that sodium and calcium ions can enter the cell.

6. Calcium ions induce the expression of otherwise inactive genes that produce proteins that alter the activities of more than a hundred other known chemicals within the dendrites. This increases the future responsiveness of these glutamate receptors.

7. Calcium enhances the responsiveness to glutamate by activating a protein called CaMKII, leading to the following effects:

   a. The AMPA receptors add a phosphate group, becoming more sensitive to glutamate.

   b. Some silent receptors change into functional AMPA receptors.

   c. The dendrite may build more AMPA receptors or move them into a better position.

   d. Neurons make more NMDA receptors.

   e. The dendrite may make more branches, thus forming additional synapses with the same axon.

8. Once LTP has been established, it no longer depends on NMDA synapses. Drugs that block NMDA prevent the establishment of LTP, but they do not interfere with the maintenance of LTP.

9. LTP causes presynaptic changes through the release of a retrograde neurotransmitter from the postsynaptic cell. These changes include reduced threshold for producing action potentials, increased neurotransmitter release, and increased production of GAP-43.

10. The relationship between LTP and learning is unknown at this time, however studying the biochemistry of LTP has improved our understanding of what could impair or improve memory.

Class Activities and Demonstrations

1. Distinguishing Episodic, Semantic, and Procedural memories: Make copies of the handout on pg. 131 and give it to your students. Remind students that episodic and semantic memories fall under the category of declarative memories (memories that a person can state in words), whereas procedural memories are motor skill memories.

2. Demonstration: The Mini-Mental Status Examination: This is an evaluation scale developed by Evelyn Lee Teng and others (1987) and is often used to diagnose dementia. Allow students to examine this test in order to review the various impairments associated with Alzheimer's disease and other dementias. Many questions found on this examination will seem quite simple to students, but remind them that individuals suffering from dementia, particularly in the later stages, are often challenged by such problems.

   Source: Teng, E. L., Chui, H. C., Schneider, L. S., and Metzger, L. E. (1987). Mini-mental status examination. *Journal of Consulting and Clinical Psychology*, *55*, 96-100.

Class Activities and Demonstrations from Exploring Biological Psychology CD-ROM

Try It Yourself Demonstrations

   Implicit Memories
   Long-Term Potentiation

Print Supplements

Study Guide: Chapter 13

Multimedia Resources

CNN® Today Video

1. Alzheimer's Disease and the Brain, Volume 1, Segment 8 (2:05 min).
2. Predicting Alzheimer's Disease, Volume 1, Segment 18 (2:13 min).

VIDEOS

1. Fires of the Mind (Insight Media, 58 min): Video presents studies on the formation of synaptic connections and memory encoding as a way to understand how humans learn and create. It also considers the role of neuroglia in human brain functioning.

2. Learning and Memory (Insight Media, 34 min): Examines the scientific explanations of short- and long-term memory using memory research with fruit flies, snails, monkeys, and humans.

3. Memory: Fabric of the Mind (Films for the Humanities and Sciences, 28 min): Includes conversations with renowned memory researchers Gary Lynch, James McGaugh, Richard Thompson, and John Hopfield about the latest discoveries in neuronal mechanisms of memory.

4. Memory (Insight Media, 30 min): This film explores the three stages of memory (encoding, storage, and retrieval) and discusses several models of memory. In addition, the video covers many phenomena related to memory, such as flashbulb memories, retroactive interference, and displacement and decay of memory.

CD-ROM

Exploring Biological Psychology
    Classical Conditioning (video)
    Amnestic Patient (video)
    Alzheimer's Patient (video)
    Neural Networks and Memory (video)
    Critical Thinking (essay questions)
    Chapter Quiz (multiple choice questions)

Related Web Sites

http://psychology.wadsworth.com/kalatbiopsych8e

On-line quizzes, weblinks, and more.

http://brembs.net/

Interesting web site on the neuroscience of classical and instrumental conditioning in the *drosophilae* (fruit fly). Lots of good background information on these learning paradigms.

http://www.diseases.nu/amnesia.htm

List of links on the causes and treatments of amnesia from the Disease Information Center.

http://www.exploratorium.edu/memory/index.html

Exploratorium: The Memory Exhibition — This site explores the biological, psychological, and cultural aspects of memory — from personal experiences to breakthroughs in cognitive science. Online Exhibits focus on memory, with memory tips and demonstrations. The Sheep Brain Dissection explores the anatomy of memory. Articles provide additional information.

http://www.ultranet.com/~jkimball/BiologyPages/L/LTP.html

A good concise explanation of the process of LTP from Dr. John Kimball's biology pages.

http://www.memorylossonline.com/index.htm

This is the online version of <u>Memory Loss and the Brain,</u> the free newsletter of the Memory Disorders Project at Rutgers University. This site has easy to understand articles on the latest findings in cognitive neuroscience and neuropsychology as it relates to memory loss. It also has great links to other information in its resources section.

InfoTrac Key Terms for Class Discussion or Papers

1. **False Memories**: Have students research this controversial issue and discuss what this means about how we store and retrieve old memories.

2. **Memory and Imaging**: Have students examine the current research on memory storage and retrieval based on brain imaging technology.

3. **Neuroplasticity**: New research seems to indicate that our brains are in a state of constant reorganization based on new inputs. Have students read and discuss the research on neuroplasticity

Critical Thinking Exercises

LTP and Memory

Long-term potentiation (LTP) is one of the most studied phenomena in neuroscience. The tremendous interest in this effect is due to its hypothesized relationship to memory formation. Have students research the literature on LTP and debate the usefulness of this model in understanding memory.

Enriched Environments

Research in animals has demonstrated that early sensory stimulation increases the number of synaptic connections and improves performance on many cognitive tasks. Have students discuss possible mechanisms involved in this task improvement and discuss the possible relevance of this research to humans.

Author's Answers to Thought Questions

1. Lashley sought to find the engram, the physiological representation of learning. In general terms, how would you recognize an engram if you saw one? That is, what would someone have to demonstrate before you could conclude that a particular change in the nervous system was really an engram?

   To identify any physical change as an engram, I would test whether the change met the following criteria: (a) The physical change should occur over the same time course as the behavioral changes identified as learning. (b) The same physical change should not occur in an adequate control group. (c) Drugs or other procedures that retard, promote, or remove the physical change should have corresponding effects on behavior.

2. Benzodiazepine tranquilizers impair memory. Use what you have learned in this chapter and the previous one to propose an explanation.

    Emotionally arousing events increase activity in the amygdala, which facilitates storage of memories. Benzodiazepines facilitate activity of the inhibitory transmitter GABA in the amygdala and thereby decrease amygdala activity.

3. If a synapse has already developed LTP once, should it be easier or more difficult to get it to develop LTP again? Why?

    It should be easier. LTP increases the responsiveness of AMPA receptors. Therefore, a new burst of glutamate at the synapses should excite these receptors more than usual, therefore depolarizing the membrane enough to activate nearby NMDA receptors and initiating a new round of LTP.

Distinguishing Episodic, Semantic, and Procedural Memories

Below you will find a list of situations. Read each one carefully and decide if it is an example of episodic, semantic, or procedural memory.

E = Episodic (Autobiographical memory; memory for events that happened directly to you)
S = Semantic (Memory for facts or knowledge not directly related to you)
P = Procedural (Memory for motor skills)

1.	Riding a bike.	E S P
2.	Describing your trip to Las Vegas on New Year's Eve.	E S P
3.	Naming the capital of Michigan.	E S P
4.	Stating what you were doing when the Challenger space shuttle exploded.	E S P
5.	Driving a car home from school.	E S P
6.	Being able to read and play music.	E S P
7.	Describing what you had for breakfast this morning.	E S P
8.	Stating the 12 cranial nerves (in order).	E S P
9.	Recalling events from your 10th birthday.	E S P
10.	Playing tennis or golf.	E S P

CHAPTER 14

LATERALIZATION AND LANGUAGE

Chapter Outline

I. **Lateralization of Function**

    A. The brain has two hemispheres; each hemisphere controls the contralateral (opposite) side of the body. For example, the right hemisphere is connected to sensory receptors and muscles mainly on the left half of the body (the opposite holds true for the left hemisphere).

    B. **Corpus Callosum**: A set of axons which allow the two hemispheres to exchange information with one another.

    C. **Lateralization**: Refers to those behaviors and cognitive abilities that each hemisphere specializes in. For example, language ability is primarily localized in the left hemisphere.

    D. Visual and Auditory Connections to the Hemispheres

        1. Light from the right **visual field** (what is visible at a particular moment) shines onto the left half of both retinas; this information is then relayed to the left hemisphere. The right half of each retina connects to the right hemisphere, which sees the left visual field.

        2. **Optic chiasm**: Point where half of the axons from each eye cross to the opposite side of the brain.

        3. Each ear receives sound waves from one side of the head, but each sends the information to both sides of the brain. If the two ears receive different information, each hemisphere pays more attention to the ear on the opposite side.

    E. Cutting the Corpus Callosum

        1. Severing the corpus callosum prevents the sharing of information between the brain hemispheres.

        2. **Epilepsy**: Condition characterized by repeated episodes of excessive synchronized neural activity (i.e., seizure). Most people with epilepsy (90%) use drugs to suppress their seizure activity.

        3. If seizure activity is not controlled by drug therapy, some people have surgery to remove the **focus** (point of origin of the seizure). Alternatively, epileptics sometimes have their corpus callosum severed to prevent seizure activity from crossing from one hemisphere to the other. These individuals are often referred to as **split-brain people**.

        4. Split-brain people can point to objects with their left hand (but not with their right hand) if visual information is presented from the left visual field to their right hemisphere. Information presented in the right visual field (thus going to the left hemisphere) allows patients to name or describe what they see.

        5. The two hemispheres of a split-brain person can process information independently of each other. However, the brain eventually learns to use smaller connections between the left and right hemispheres to avoid conflicts between them.

        6. The Right Hemisphere

      a.   The right hemisphere is better than the left at perceiving the emotions in people's gestures and one of voice.

      b.   People with right hemisphere damage speak with less inflection and expression, plus they often have trouble interpreting the emotions that other people express through their tone of voice.

      c.   Research findings suggest that the right hemisphere is more adept than the left at comprehending spatial relationships.

      d.   The left hemisphere is more focused on details and the right hemisphere is better at perceiving overall patterns.

7.   Differences in hemisphere specialization can be demonstrated in people without brain damage, but most of these differences are apparent only as averages over large numbers of people.

F.   Development of Lateralization and Handedness

1.   **Planum temporale**: A section of the temporal cortex that is larger in the left hemisphere in approximately 65% of the population. This difference in size is apparent at age 3 months in humans. Children with the biggest ratio of left to right planum temporale performed best on language tests.

2.   The corpus callosum matures slowly over the first 5 to 10 years of human life. Because the neurons connected by the corpus callosum take years to develop their mature adult pattern, the behavior of young children sometimes resembles that of split-brain people.

3.   People born without a corpus callosum can perform some tasks that split-brain people fail, possibly due to larger-than-normal hemispheric connections developing elsewhere in the brain. For example, they can describe what they feel with either hand and what they see in either visual field. The following two commissures are often larger than normal in people born without a corpus callosum:

      a.   **Anterior commissure**: Connects the two hemispheres around the anterior parts of the cerebral cortex.

      b.   **Hippocampal commissure**: Connects the left hippocampus to the right hippocampus.

4.   Most people (90%) are right handed and in this group, the left hemisphere is dominant for speech. Left handed people are more variable. Most left handers have a left hemisphere dominance for speech, but some have right hemisphere dominance or a mixture of left and right. The corpus callosum is larger in left handers than in right handers.

5.   Recovery of speech after brain damage depends on what hemisphere is damaged and how speech was lateralized. For example, a person with speech lateralized to the left hemisphere would have a language impairment after suffering left hemisphere damage, but not right hemisphere damage. Someone with bilateral representation of language would suffer mild deficits after damage to either hemisphere, but would recover quickly.

6.   Children with left-hemisphere damage generally recover more language than adults with similar damage, but the age of the child is less important than the cause of the damage.

7. **Rasmussen's encephalopathy**: a rare autoimmune disorder that attacks the glia and neurons of one hemisphere of the brain. Language recovery is surprising good for children with this disorder.

II. Evolution and Physiology of Language

A. Human language is unique because of it **productivity**, its ability to produce new signals to represent new ideas.

B. Nonhuman precursors to language
1. Common chimpanzees can not learn to talk, but can learn some language skills using American Sign Language or other visual systems.   Their use of language-related symbols differ from human language in many ways:
    a. The chimpanzees seldom used the symbols in new original combinations.
    b. The chimpanzees used their symbols almost always to make a request, only rarely to describe.
    c. The chimpanzees produced requests far better than they seem to understand anyone else's request.
2. Bonobos (*Pan paniscus*) given language training used symbols in several ways that more resemble humans than common chimpanzees:
    a. They understood more information than they produce.
    b. They use symbols to name and describe objects even when they are not requesting them.
    c. They request items that they do not see.
    d. They occasionally use the symbols to describe past events.
    e. They frequently make original, creative requests.
3. The reason for the better language skills in the bonobos is unknown, but three reasons have been suggested:
    a. Bonobos have more language potential than common chimpanzees.
    b. The bonobos trained so far have been very young, unlike the chimpanzees in other studies.
    c. The bonobos trained so far have learned by observation and imitation rather than formal language training.
4. Alex, an African gray parrot, can say a variety of words in conjunction with specific objects. Alex's language abilities have caused many to rethink some assumptions about what sort of brain development is necessary for language.

C. How Did Humans Evolve Language
1. Language as a Product of Overall Intelligence
    a. The relationship between brain and brain-to-body ratio is unclear. **Chihuahua problem**: Chihuahuas have the highest brain-to-body ratio of all dogs. Does that make them the smartest of dogs? Many animals have larger brains and brain-to-body ratios than human, but do not have human language abilities.
    b. Presumably because of a dominant gene, 16 people of normal intelligence within one family have severe difficulty with pronunciation, and all other aspects of language. Cases such as this suggest that genetic conditions which affect brain development can impair language without impacting other aspects of intelligence.

c. **Williams syndrome**: A rare disorder in which retarded individuals have skillful use of language, but limited abilities in other regards. This disorder is caused by a deletion of several genes from chromosome 7.

2. Language as a Special Module
   a. An alternate view of the evolution of language is that language evolved as an extra brain module, called a **language acquisition device**. This idea is supported by the fact that children learn language with amazing ease and that children learn language despite the fact they do not hear enough examples to learn the grammatical structure of language (this is called the **poverty of the stimulus argument**).
   b. Language has a critical period, because if you don't learn language when you are young, you will forever be language disadvantaged.

D. Brain Damage and Language
   1. **Aphasia**: Severe language impairment
   2. **Broca's area**: Small part of the frontal lobe of the left cerebral cortex that when damaged leads to language impairments.
   3. **Broca's aphasia** or **nonfluent aphasia**: A language impairment whose most prominent symptom is a deficit in language production. Caused by damage to Broca' area and surrounding areas.
      a. Patients suffering from Broca's aphasia speak meaningfully, but omit pronouns, prepositions, conjunctions, and qualifiers from their own speech; they also have trouble understanding these same kinds of words.
   4. **Wernicke's aphasia** or **fluent aphasia**: Damage to Wernicke's Area, near the auditory part of the temporal cortex, leads to difficulty in comprehending the verbal and written communications of others. Although patients can still speak smoothly, their speech content is often nonsensical. They also have **anomia** (difficulty recalling the names of objects).
   5. Language requires the activation of many different areas other than the frontal cortex (Broca's area and surrounding regions) and the temporal cortex (Wernicke's area).

E. Dyslexia
   1. **Dyslexia**: Inability to read despite adequate vision and intelligence. Many kinds of dyslexia exist with different underlying causes.
   2. As a rule, a dyslexic person is more likely to have a bilaterally symmetrical cerebral cortex (i.e., the planum temporale and other structures are the same size on the left and right hemisphere).
   3. Different researchers have hypothesized different explanations for dyslexia including:
      a. Dyslexic people have an unresponsive magnocellular path to the visual system.
      b. Dyslexia reflects a subtle hearing impairment.
      c. Dyslexia is caused by a problem converting vision to sound or vice versa, as if one part of the brain were poorly connected to another.
      d. Dyslexia is a function of attentional differences.

Class Activities and Demonstrations

Which Hemisphere Are You Using? Begin this exercise by asking 3-6 volunteers to leave the room. Explain to the rest of the class that you will ask the subjects a series of questions and the class should try and observe the subjects' eye movements while they ponder them. Assign a few students to be the official observers for specific subjects. Afterwards, bring the volunteers to the front of the class and ask them to focus on the back wall while they try to silently solve a number of problems.

Problems:

1. What is meant by the proverb "A bird in the hand is worth two in the bush"?
2. Define the word "vulnerable".
3. Tell me an English word that begins with R and ends with E.
4. A zookeeper has 3 flamingoes and 4 elephants at the zoo. How many feet are at his zoo?
5. There is a profile of Abraham Lincoln on a penny. Which way does he face?
6. How many corners are in a solid cube?
7. You are heading north. You make two right turns and then a left turn. In what direction are you now heading?
8. Name three states that border Colorado.

Have the observers report the direction of the eye gaze of each subject for each problem. Two trends should be observed:

- Questions 1-4: These are considered left hemisphere questions; eye movements should be to the right.

- Questions 5-8: These are considered right hemisphere questions; eye movements should be to the left.

Source: Townsend-Merino, K. (1996). Which hemisphere are you using? *Instructor's resource guide for Plotnik's Introduction to Psychology*, 4th edition. Pacific Grove: Brooks/Cole.

Class Activities and Demonstrations from Exploring Biological Psychology CD-ROM

Try It Yourself Demonstrations

      Hemisphere Control
      Hemispheric Specialization

Print Supplements

Study Guide: Chapter 14

Multimedia Resources

VIDEOS

1. The Sinister Hand: A Look at Left-Handedness (Films from the Humanities and Sciences, 28 min): In this thought-provoking program, academic and medical experts explore cultural, physiological, hormonal, and genetic theories of handedness. The connection between hand dominance and language control is also examined, as well as the association of left-handedness with enhanced spatial perception and emotional expression.

2. Broken English: The Effects of Brain Damage on Language (Films from the Humanities and Sciences, 47 min): Video examines the effect of damage to both Broca's and Wernicke's areas on patients' ability to communicate verbally and through sign language. The video also covers different areas of research in language including the new field of neurolinguistics.

3. Man in the Mirror (Films from the Humanities and Sciences, 60 min): This video examines the chiral (handed) nature of humans. It examines brain lateralization, handedness, and different asymmetric properties of human physiology.

4. Chimp Talk (Films for the Humanities and Sciences, 13 min): In this program, Paul Hoffman, editor of Discover magazine, explores the controversial issue of language use by apes with primatologist Dr. Sue Savage-Rumbaugh and Dr. Laura Ann Petitto.

5. Don't Be Shy, Mr. Sacks: Williams Syndrome (Films for the Humanities and Sciences, 50 min): In this film, Dr. Sacks probes the nature of Williams syndrome. What he discovers sheds new light on the genetic basis of personality and provides fascinating insights into how the brain organizes data and experiences. A BBC Production.

CD-ROM

Exploring Biological Psychology
    Lateralization and Language (animation)
    Critical Thinking (essay questions)
    Chapter Quiz (multiple choice questions)

Related Web Sites

---

http://psychology.wadsworth.com/kalatbiopsych8e

    On-line quizzes, weblinks, and more.

http://www.indiana.edu/~primate/brain.html

This is good site for obtaining additional information about the relationship between handedness and brain lateralization. The site is the work of M. K. Holder, Director of the Handedness Research Institute at Indiana University.

http://www.aphasia.org/

Homepage of the National Aphasia Association. This site has a lot of information on the different types of aphasia and good links to other resources.

http://williamcalvin.com/bk7/bk7.htm

Conversations with Neil's Brain: The Neural Nature of Thought & Language by William H. Calvin and George A. Ojemann. This is a fascinating book about a conversation with a patient named Neil during brain surgery to treat his epilepsy.

http://faculty.washington.edu/chudler/lang.html

Dr. Chudler's web site gives a good overview of language, including non human communication, anatomical locations, and disorders of language.

http://faculty.washington.edu/chudler/split.html

Dr. Chudler gives a nice overview of split brain research and has great links to other web resources on the topic.

InfoTrac Key Terms for Class Discussion or Papers

1. **Handedness**: Have students review the literature on handedness. Especially, interesting are the correlations between handedness and language disorders and premature death.

2. **Cerebral Dominance**: Have students read current research on brain lateralization and discuss the relevance of knowing what hemisphere is dominant for certain functions.

3. **Animal Communication**—Subdivision Research: Language skills in non humans are a much debated question. Have students read the literature on animal language and discuss whether they believe nonhumans can learn language.

4. **Dyslexia**: Have students research the causes and treatments for this language disorder.

Critical Thinking Exercises

What Is the Function of Language?

Language appears to be a unique ability of humans. Have students discuss the function of language in human societies. Have students especially examine the possibility that language serves some unique role not found in other types of animal communication.

Gender and Reading Disorders

Boys are over represented in the population of children with reading disorders. Have students discuss whether differences in lateralization account for the greater amount of language disability. Moreover, ask students to discuss whether boys have some advantages due to the greater lateralization.

Author's Answers to Thought Questions

1. When a person born without a corpus callosum moves the fingers of one hand, he or she is likely also to move the fingers of the other hand, involuntarily. What possible explanation can you suggest?

   In such people, each hemisphere may develop pathways linking it to both sides of the body. The spinal pathway to one hand may have branches connecting to the other hand; thus, moving one hand causes movement of the other hand.

2. Most people with Broca's aphasia suffer from partial paralysis on the right side of the body. Most people with Wernicke's aphasia do not. Why?

   Broca's area is close to the motor cortex in the left frontal lobe; Wernicke's area is not. Damage that includes Broca's area is likely to overlap part of the motor cortex as well.

3. In a syndrome called "word blindness," a person loses the ability to read (even single letters), although the person can still see and speak. What is a possible neurological explanation?

   Information from the visual areas of the cortex cannot reach the language areas. This pattern of behavior occurs after damage to the left visual cortex (occipital lobe) and the posterior corpus callosum. The remaining right visual cortex can see and the language areas of the left hemisphere can talk, but the visual information cannot readily reach the left hemisphere.

CHAPTER 15

PSYCHOLOGICAL DISORDERS

Chapter Outline

I. **Substance Abuse**

   A. **Substance Abuse:** A maladaptive pattern of substance use leading to clinically significant impairment of distress as defined by the APA (1994) in the DSM-IV (p. 182).

   B. Synapses, Reinforcement, and Drug Use
      1. Olds and Milner (1954) conducted the first brain reinforcement experiments by implanting electrodes in the brains of rats and allowing them to press a lever to produce **self-stimulation of the brain**.
         a. Later experiments showed that the reinforcing brain stimulation almost exclusively activated tracts of axons that release dopamine, especially in an area called the **nucleus accumbens**. Cells located in the nucleus accumbens are inhibited by increased DA activity (most abused drugs, as well as ordinary pleasures, lead to increased DA activity); some hypothesize that this phenomenon occurs with drug addiction.
         b. Because of its role in reinforcement the nucleus accumbens is regarded by many as the pleasure area and dopamine as the pleasure chemical. However, several lines of evidence conflict with this interpretation and more recent studies suggest that dopamine and the nucleus accumbens play an important role in attention-getting or arousal.

   C. Common Drugs and Their Synaptic Effects
      1. **Stimulant drugs** (e.g., amphetamines, cocaine, etc.) produce excitement, alertness, elevated mood, decreased fatigue, and sometimes motor activity. Each of these drugs increases activity at dopamine receptors, especially at D_2, D_3, and D_4 receptors. Stimulant drugs are often highly addictive.
         a. **Amphetamine** increases dopamine release from presynaptic terminals by reversing the direction of the dopamine transporter.
         b. **Cocaine** blocks the reuptake of catecholamines and serotonin at the synapse. The behavioral effects of cocaine are believed to be mediated primarily by dopamine and secondarily by serotonin.
         c. The effects of amphetamine and cocaine are both short-lived, because of the depletion of dopamine stores and tolerance.
         d. **Methylphenidate** (Ritalin): Stimulant currently prescribed for Attention Deficit Disorder (ADD); works like cocaine by blocking reuptake of dopamine at presynaptic terminals. The effects of methylphenidate are much longer lasting and less intense as compared to cocaine.
         e. Repeated use of stimulants, such as cocaine or MDMA (ecstasy), can have permanent effects on brain functioning.

2. **Nicotine**: Compound found in tobacco. Stimulates the nicotinic receptor (a type of acetylcholine receptor) both in the central nervous system and neuromuscular junction of skeletal muscles; can also increase dopamine release by attaching to neurons that release dopamine in the nucleus accumbens.

3. **Opiate Drugs**: Derived from (or similar to those derived from) the opium poppy. Common opiates include morphine, heroin, and methadone. Opiates have a net effect of increasing the release of dopamine by stimulating *endorphin* receptors. Opiates also decrease activity in the locus coeruleus which results in decreased response to stress and decreased memory storage.

4. **Marijuana**: Contains the chemical Δ^9-tetrahydrocannabionol (Δ^9-THC) and other **cannabinoids** (chemicals related to Δ^9-THC); Δ^9-THC works by attaching to cannabinoid receptors. **Anandamide** is a brain chemical that binds to cannabinoid receptors.

5. **Hallucinogenic drugs**: Drugs that distort perception. Many hallucinogenic drugs resemble serotonin and bind to serotonin type 2A (5-HT_{2A}) receptors.

D. Alcohol and Alcoholism

1. **Alcoholism** or **alcohol dependence**: A common type of substance abuse that produces significant harm to people's lives, and those people often find themselves continuing to drink in excess even after deciding to quit or reduce their drinking.

2. **Alcohol**: Inhibits Na^+ ion flow across the neuron membrane; decreases serotonin activity, facilitates transmission at the $GABA_A$ receptor, blocks glutamate receptors, and increases dopamine activity.

3. Researchers distinguish two major types of alcoholism:

   a. **Type I** (or Type A) **Alcoholism**: This type of alcoholism is less dependent on genetic factors, develops gradually over years, affects men and women equally, and is generally less severe.

   b. **Type II** (or Type B) **Alcoholism**: This type of alcoholism has a strong genetic basis, a rapid and early onset, affects men primarily, is more severe, and more associated with criminality.

4. Alcohol Metabolism and Antabuse

   a. **Acetaldehyde**: A poisonous substance created when ethyl alcohol (drinking alcohol) is metabolized in the liver. Acetaldehyde is then further metabolized into **acetic acid**, a chemical the body can use as a source of energy.

   b. **Acetaldehyde dehydrogenase** is the enzyme used to convert acetaldehyde into acetic acid.

   c. Some people have an abnormal gene for acetaldehyde dehydrogenase so they metabolize alcohol slowly. Approximately 50% of people in China and Japan have the gene that slows acetaldehyde metabolism.

   d. **Anatabuse** (*disulfiram*): A drug that blocks the effects of the enzyme acetaldehyde dehydrogenase by binding to its copper ion. Anatabuse is used to treat alcoholism, because Antabuse causes the ingestion of alcohol to lead to sickness.

5. Risk Factors for Alcohol Abuse

   a. Less than average intoxication after drinking a small to moderate amount of alcohol.

   b. Experiencing more than average relief from tension after drinking alcohol.

c. Having a smaller than normal amygdala in the right hemisphere.

II. Mood Disorders

A. **Major Depression**: According to DSM-IV, people with major depression feel sad, helpless, and lacking in energy and pleasure for weeks at a time. Individuals with major depression also feel worthless, have trouble sleeping, can not concentrate, get little pleasure from sex or food, may contemplate suicide, and in many cases can hardly imagine being happy.

1. Evidence of genetic or other biological predispositions to depression exist. This is especially true if you have relatives with depression that manifests itself before age 30 or if you are a woman.

2. The most severe depression is often seen in people who have suffered a traumatic situation and are already a little depressed.

3. Depression is usually episodic, not constant; someone may feel normal for weeks, months, or years between episodes of depression.

4. Most women experience the blues for a day or two after giving birth; only about 20 percent experience postpartum depression (depression after giving birth).

5. Depression is more common among women than men, although childhood depression is equally common in boys and girls.

6. Most people suffering from depression have decreased activity in the left hemisphere and increased activity in the right prefrontal cortex.

7. **Borna disease**: Viral infection of the nervous system leading to periods of frantic activity alternating with periods of inactivity.
   a. In a study conducted in the early 1990's across three continents, 30 percent of severely depressed patients tested positive for the Borna virus; these findings, as well as those of other studies, suggest a relationship between the Borna virus and depression.

8. Antidepressant drugs: Drugs used for the treatment of depression and other mood disorders. These drugs fall into four categories:
   a. **Tricyclics**: Prevent the presynaptic neuron from reabsorbing catecholamines or serotonin after releasing them (this allows the neurotransmitter to remain longer in the synaptic cleft thus stimulating postsynaptic receptors).
   b. **Monoamine oxidase inhibitors (MAOIs)**: Block the enzyme monoamine oxidase (MAO) from metabolizing catecholamines and serotonin into inactive forms.
   c. **Selective serotonin reuptake inhibitors** (SSRIs): These drugs are similar to tricyclics, but are specific to the neurotransmitter serotonin. The most popular drug in this class is fluoxetine (Prozac).
   d. **Atypical Antidepressants**: A miscellaneous group of drugs with antidepressant actions and mild side effects, including bupropion (Wellbutrin), which inhibits reuptake of dopamine and to some extent norepinephrine; venlaxfine, which inhibits the reuptake of serotonin and norepinephrine; and nefazodone, which specifically blocks serotonin type 2A receptors and blocks reuptake of serotonin and norepinephrine.

e. Most of antidepressants have delayed effects that limit the excitation of the postsynaptic cell. One effect is to decrease the sensitivity of the postsynaptic cell. Another effect is to stimulate **autoreceptors** (a negative feedback receptor on the presynaptic terminal) decreasing further release of neurotransmitter.

f. Most antidepressants require 2 or 3 weeks before benefits begin suggesting their effects on depression are not directly mediated by their synaptic actions.. One explanation may be that antidepressants gradually increase the release of neurotrophins and cause an increase in cell size (it has been established that neurons in the hippocampus and cerebral cortex shrink in size when people are depressed).

9. Other Therapies

a. Psychotherapy and drug therapies produce similar effects on brain activity. Patients who recover using psychotherapy are less likely to relapse, but it takes twice the time to get benefits from psychotherapy as compared to drug treatments.

b. **Electroconvulsive therapy (ECT)**: Inducing seizures with an electric shock to the head. ECT is usually applied every other day for about two weeks. About half of those who respond well to ECT relapse into depression within six months unless they are given antidepressant drugs or other therapies to prevent it.

c. Most depressed people enter REM sleep within 45 minutes after going to bed compared to about 80 minutes for non-depressed people. One way to treat depression is to have the individual go to sleep earlier than usual, in phase with his or her temperature cycle; another way is to have the depressed person stay awake all night.

B. **Bipolar disorder (Manic-depression disorder)**: Disorder where the person alternates between episodes of depression and **mania** (characterized by restless activity, excitement, laughter, self-confidence, rambling speech, and loss of inhibitions).

1. **Bipolar I disorder:** A type of bipolar disorder where the person has full-blown episodes of mania.

2. **Bipolar II disorder:** A type of bipolar disorder where the person has much milder manic phases, called hypomania.

3. The mean age of onset of bipolar disorder is the late 20's.

4. In people with bipolar disorder, brain activity is higher than normal during mania and lower than normal during depression. Bipolar patients also have a larger than normal amygdala.

5. There is a strong hereditary basis for bipolar disorder, however no specific gene for this disorder has been located.

6. Lithium salts are the most effective therapy for bipolar disorder, but how it works remains unknown. Other drug treatments include anticonvulsant drugs such as valproic acid and carbamazepine. Encouraging bipolar patients to keep a consistent sleep schedule may reduce the intensity of the mood swings.

C. **Seasonal affective disorder (SAD)**: Depression that reoccurs seasonally, usually in the winter.

1. SAD is most common in regions closest to the poles, where the nights are very long in winter and very short in summer.

2.   It is possible to treat SAD by exposing the person to very bright lights for about an hour either early in the morning or in the evening.

III. Schizophrenia

A. **Schizophrenia**: A disorder characterized both by deteriorating ability to function in everyday life and by some combination of delusions, hallucinations, movement disorder, thought disorder, and inappropriate emotional expression.
    1.   Schizophrenia was originally called *dementia praecox*. Eugen Bleuler came up with the term schizophrenia in 1911, which has been preferred ever since.
    2.   Behavioral Symptoms
        a.   **Positive symptoms**: Behaviors that are present that should be absent. Positive symptoms fall into two clusters that do not correlate strongly with each other:
            •   The *psychotic* cluster of positive symptoms consists of **delusions** (unfounded beliefs) and **hallucinations** (abnormal sensory experiences).
            •   The *disorganized* cluster of positive symptoms consists of inappropriate emotions, bizarre behavior, and **thought disorder** (inability to use and understand abstract concepts).
        b.   **Negative symptoms**: Behaviors that are absent that should be present, such as deficits of social interaction and emotional expression.
    3.   Schizophrenia can be either **acute** (a sudden onset with a good possibility of returning to normal in a short time) or **chronic** (a gradual onset and a long-term course).
    4.   Differential Diagnosis of Schizophrenia
        a.   Differential Diagnosis: A diagnosis that identifies one condition as distinct from all other conditions with similar symptoms. Schizophrenia is hard to diagnose, because there are several conditions with similar symptoms including:
        b.   Mood disorder with psychotic features
        c.   Substance abuse
        d.   Brain damage
        e.   Undetected hearing loss
        f.   Huntington's disease
        g.   Nutritional abnormalities
    5.   Demographic Data
        a.   Schizophrenia occurs in all ethnic groups and about equally in men and women; however, it usually develops at an earlier age in men.
        b.   **Expressed emotions**: Hostile expressions by the caretaker of someone with schizophrenia that can aggravate the condition. Expressed emotions may be a reason for the increased number of cases in the United State and Europe, as compared to many third world countries.
        c.   The older the age of the father at time of the baby's birth, the greater the risk of schizophrenia.

B. Genetics
    1.   For monozygotic schizophrenic twins there is about a 50 percent **concordance** (agreement), and a 15% concordance for dizygotic twins. The greater concordance

in monozygotic twins does not necessarily mean a genetic cause, as a pure genetic effect would have a 100% concordance. The greater environmental similarity in monozygotic twins, as compared to dizyogotic twins, may also influence concordance rates.

2.   Adopted children who develop schizophrenia usually have adopting relatives that are psychologically normal, but a high percentage of the biological relatives have schizophrenia.

3.   Currently, there are no reliable genetic markers for schizophrenia. This inability to find a genetic link could be a result of one of the following possibilities:

a.   Our diagnosis of schizophrenia is not exact enough for genetic research.

b.   Schizophrenia is caused by a combination of genes.

c.   Schizophrenia has a number of different causes that are not all genetic, such as prenatal or postnatal environment problems.

C.   The **neurodevelopmental hypothesis**: Schizophrenia is caused in large part by abnormalities to the nervous system during the prenatal or neonatal periods.

1.   Prenatal and Neonatal Environment

a.   Many people with schizophrenia had problems before or shortly after birth that could have affected their brain development, including poor nutrition and low birth weight, and complications during delivery such as extensive maternal bleeding or prolonged labor.

b.   Schizophrenia has been linked to problems in early or middle pregnancy. During WWII, Dutch women who were on a starvation diet in the early stages of pregnancy gave birth to a high percentage of babies who later developed schizophrenia.

c.   Rh incompatibility between mom and offspring is associated with increased probability of schizophrenia, especially in boys and later-born babies.

d.   **Season-of-birth effect**: Tendency for those born in winter to have a slightly greater probability of developing schizophrenia; this tendency occurs only in nontropical climates. Many scientists believe that a viral infection during a fall pregnancy accounts for the season-of-birth effect.

2.   Mild Brain Abnormalities

a.   MRI studies reveal that many schizophrenics have a slightly smaller prefrontal cortex, temporal cortex, hippocampus, and amygdala than non-schizophrenic adults. They also have larger than normal ventricles.

b.   The areas of the brain that most consistently show signs of abnormality in schizophrenics are the ones that mature the most slowly, such as the prefrontal cortex.

c.   At a microscopic level people with schizophrenia have smaller than normal cell bodies and some of their neurons fail to arrange themselves in the neat orderly manner of normal brains.

d.   People suffering from schizophrenia have slightly larger right hemispheres; while non-schizophrenic adults tend to have larger left hemispheres. Schizophrenics also have lower than normal overall activity in the left hemisphere.

3.   An important issue related to the neurodevelopmental hypothesis is why do the symptoms show up after 20 years of age if the damage occurs early in brain

development. It is currently thought that the early brain damage is done in areas that are slow to mature, such as the prefrontal cortex for this reason the damage produces only minor symptoms in childhood, but increasing impairments when the brain area fully matures.

D. Neurotransmitters and Drugs
1. **Dopamine hypothesis of schizophrenia:** According to this hypothesis, schizophrenia results from excess activity at certain dopamine synapses. The primary evidence for this hypothesis is the type of drugs that relieve and aggravate the symptoms of schizophrenia.
   a. **Chlorpromazine** (Thorazine): First drug used successfully for the treatment of schizophrenia.
   b. **Antipsychotic drugs (neuroleptic drugs)**: Drugs used for the treatment of schizophrenia. These drugs work primarily by blocking dopamine receptors.
      - **Phenothiazines**: A class of neuroleptic drugs, which includes chlorpromazine.
      - **Butyrophenones**: A class of neuroleptic drugs which includes haloperidol (Haldol).
   c. **Substance-induced psychotic disorder**: Disorder characterized by hallucinations and delusions caused by drugs such as cocaine, amphetamine, and LSD that increase the activity of dopamine synapses.
   d. Stress exacerbates the symptoms of schizophrenia and causes the release of dopamine from the prefrontal cortex, an area believed to be important in schizophrenia.
   e. Excess production and release of dopamine cannot be the sole cause of schizophrenia. Drugs that block dopamine receptors do so almost immediately, but their effects on behavior build up gradually over 2 or 3 weeks. Also, levels of dopamine and its metabolites are generally normal in schizophrenics. Furthermore, the research on dopamine receptors has yielded complicated results that are hard to interpret.
   f. A recent studies has indicated that schizophrenic people have about twice as many D_2 receptors occupied by dopamine as normal people.
2. **Glutamate hypothesis of schizophrenia**: Idea that schizophrenia results from deficient activity at certain glutamate synapses. Because dopamine inhibits glutamate activity in many parts of the brain, much of the evidence supporting the dopamine hypothesis of schizophrenia also supports the glutamate hypothesis of schizophrenia.
   a. Researchers have found that the brains of schizophrenic people release lower than normal amounts of glutamate in the prefrontal cortex and hippocampus. Schizophrenics also have fewer glutamate receptors.
   b. **Phencyclidine (PCP)**: A drug that blocks glutamate type NMDA receptors. PCP administration produces a type of psychosis more similar to schizophrenia than drugs like cocaine as PCP induces both negative and positive symptoms. Moreover, PCP does not produce psychosis in preadolescents and PCP produces a much more severe psychosis in people with a history of schizophrenia.

c.   Because increasing glutamate activity in the brain would be extremely risky, there are no drugs used to treat schizophrenia which directly stimulate glutamate activity. However, there are some experimental compounds that may someday be used to treat schizophrenia, such as the metabotropic glutamate agonist, *LY 354740*, which blocks the behavioral effects of PCP in rats and prevents PCP-induced disruption of activity in the prefrontal cortex. Another possibility is the amino acid glycine, which enhances the effects of glutamate at NMDA synapses.

3.   The Search for Improved Drugs
a.   **Mesolimbocortical system**: A set of neurons which project from the midbrain tegmentum to the limbic system. The mesolimbocortical system is believed to be the area in which antipsychotics have their beneficial effects.
b.   **Tardive dyskinesia**: A serious side effect of antipsychotics; this disorder is characterized by tremors and other involuntary movements. Tardive dyskinesia is probably due to denervation supersensitivity caused by the prolonged blockade of dopamine receptors.
c.   **Atypical antipsychotics**: New drugs (e.g., clozapine) that alleviate the symptoms of schizophrenia while seldom, if ever, producing movement problems. These drugs have less intense effects on dopamine type D_2 receptors, but stronger effects at D_4 and serotonin $5\text{-}HT_2$ receptors.
d.   Atypical antipsychotics alleviate both positive and negative symptoms of schizophrenia. Unfortunately, these compounds have their own side effects, including increased risk of diabetes and an impairment of the immune system.

Class Activities and Demonstrations

1. Survey on Drug Use/Abuse Patterns: Many students believe that drug use and abuse have declined dramatically over the years, regardless of the drug type or classification (e.g., licit vs. illicit, hallucinogens vs. stimulants, etc.). One way to foster discussion on this topic is to ask students to complete the survey on pg. 153 developed by Dr. George F. Koob of the University of California, San Diego, Department of Psychology, before discussing Chapter 15. Dr. Koob has compiled the survey results from his Drugs, Addiction, and Mental Disorder classes for more than a decade and shares indications of certain trends in drug use with his students each year. A good follow-up assignment would allow students to research articles addressing the prevalence of drug use among certain populations (e.g. 18-24 year old male vs. female smoking rates, etc.). Have students determine if the survey results match what the scientific literature concludes regarding drug use in the U.S.?

2. A Self-Rating Depression Scale: A self-assessment inventory was developed by Zung (1965) to measure the feelings and physical factors associated with depression (e.g., changes in eating and sleeping habits, lethargy, etc.). The scale takes only a few minutes to complete.

   Source: Zung, W. (1965). A self-rating depression scale. *Archives of General Psychiatry*, *12*, 63-70.

3. Symptoms of schizophrenia: Osberg (1992) developed a monologue which simulates the thought disorders and disorganized language typical of schizophrenia. Osberg recommends displaying the monologue on an overhead projector and then asking students to identify examples of specific schizophrenic symptoms.

   Source: Osberg, T.M. (1992). The disordered monologue: A classroom demonstration of the symptoms of schizophrenia. *Teaching of Psychology*, *19*, 47-48.

Print Supplements

Study Guide: Chapter 15

Multimedia Resources

CNN® Today Video

1. Ecstasy and the Brain, Volume 1, Segment 3 (1:46 min)
2. Fighting Addiction, Volume 1, Segment 13 (2:08 min)
3. Promising Future for a Person with Schizophrenia, Volume 1, Segment 16 (4:33 min)

VIDEOS

1. The Hijacked Brain (Films for the Humanities and Sciences, 57 min): An examination of research into the chemistry of addiction and its possible genetic components. This film is not specific for alcoholism, but most of the genetic studies deal specifically with alcoholism.

2. Under the Influence: The Science of Drug Abuse (Insight Media, 25 min): Overview of the effects of drugs on the brain. Has some neat pictures of brain scans from people on different types of drugs.

3. Depression: Biology of the Blues (Films from the Humanities and Sciences, 26 min): This video examines the biology of depression, including changes in neurotransmitter systems, how drug therapies work, genetic factors in depression, and how ECT treatment affects the brain.

4. Bipolar Disorder (Insight Media, 29 min): This video illustrates the different symptoms of mania and hypomania. It also describes the treatments used for this disorder, including mood stabilizers, family education, and short-term psychotherapy.

5. Schizophrenia: Causation (Insight Media, 28 min): Video presents different theories of the causes of schizophrenia including genetics and environmental factors. The video also discusses the types of functional and structural changes in the brain found in schizophrenics.

6. Unlocking the Secrets of Schizophrenia (Films from the Humanities and Sciences, 21 min): A documentary that overviews the causes of schizophrenia, how it is treated, and how people are trying to improve the lives of people with this disorder. The video includes conversations with researchers from the National Institutes of Health and a conversation with a United States senator about government efforts to understand and deal with this disorder.

CD-ROM

Exploring Biological Psychology
    Understanding Addiction (video)
    CNS Stimulants (animation)
    Opiate Narcotics (animation)
    Barbara 1 (video)
    Barbara 2 (video)
    Mary 1 (video)
    Mary 2 (video)
    Mary 3 (video)
    Frontal Neglect and the Wisconsin Card Sorting Task (video)
    Schizophrenia (video)
    Etta 1 (video)
    Etta 2 (video)
    Critical Thinking (essay questions)
    Chapter Quiz (multiple choice questions)

Related Web Sites

http://psychology.wadsworth.com/kalatbiopsych8e

On-line quizzes, weblinks, and more.

http://www.nida.nih,gov/DrugAbuse.html

The web page for the National Institute of Drug Abuse (NIDA). This is the best place to get the latest information on most common drugs of abuse.

http://www.niaaa.nih.gov/

The home page of the National Institute for Alcohol Abuse and Alcoholism. You can find anything you want to know about alcoholism on this site.

http://www.brainwiring.com/html/depression.html

This is a good comprehensive site for information on major depression and bipolar disorder.

http://athealth.com/Practitioner/Newsletter/FPN_3_2.html#3

Informative site on seasonal affective disorder from the athealth.com site.

http://www.mhsource.com/bipolar/

Comprehensive site on bipolar disorder with an impressive amount of additional links. This page is part of the Mental Health InfoSource site.

http://www.priory.com/schizo.htm

Comprehensive site on schizophrenia from the Psychiatry On-line web page.

http://www.health-center.com/mentalhealth/schizophrenia/default.htm

Easy to read, but informative site, on schizophrenia from Health-Center.com.

http://www.schizophrenia.com/

A fairly comprehensive list of web sites related to schizophrenia.

InfoTrac Key Terms for Class Discussion or Papers

1. **Drug Legalization**: After learning how addictive drugs work, have students research the arguments for legalizing drugs and debate whether drugs such as cocaine should be legalized based on their effects on the brain.

2. **Naltrexone and Alcoholism**: Naltrexone and other anti-craving medications are rapidly becoming standard treatments for alcoholism. Have students research and discuss how naltrexone decreases alcohol intake and how effective this treatment is.

3. **Wernicke's Encephalopathy**: Wernicke's encephalopathy is a disorder common in alcoholics that is caused by a thiamine deficiency. Have students research the symptoms and prevalence of this disorder.

4. **Postpartum Depression**: Depression after childbirth can be debilitating for some women. Have students discuss this special type of depression and what biochemical changes in the body could possibly account for it.

5. **Childhood-Onset Schizophrenia**: Schizophrenia with onset in childhood is a rare disorder. Have students research the differences in this type of schizophrenia versus the more common adult-onset type. Have students discuss how this disorder supports or conflicts with the popular neurodevelopmental hypothesis of schizophrenia.

Critical Thinking Exercises

What about Nicotine?

Have students research the addictive properties and the health consequences of using nicotine. Then have them debate whether it is appropriate for nicotine to be legal.

Recognizing Bipolar Depression

Bipolar depression is a particularly hard disorder to recognize because most people do not realize they periodically exhibit mania. In fact, since increased confidence and elevated mood are symptoms of this phase, it is rare for a person to seek care when manic. Have students discuss how they would screen potential sufferers of this disorder if they worked in a mental health facility—keeping in mind that most of these patients coming to a care provider are reporting symptoms of depression (i.e., in their depressed phase), anxiety and agitation (hypomanic episode), or may seem psychotic (severe manic episode).

Author's Answers to Thought Questions

1. Some people who use MDMA ("ecstasy") report that after repeated use it becomes less effective. Offer an explanation other than the usual mechanisms of tolerance that apply to other drugs.

   MDMA strongly stimulates serotonin synapses, but can also damage them. Therefore, on later occasions of use, the drug has fewer receptors available for stimulation.

2. Some people have suggested that ECT relieves depression by causing people to forget the events that caused it. What evidence opposes that hypothesis?

ECT limited to just the right hemisphere is just as effective as bilateral ECT, but with very little loss of memory. If ECT relieved depression by blotting out unpleasant memories, the amount of improvement should be proportional to the amount of amnesia.

3. With some illnesses, a patient who at first fails to respond is offered higher and higher doses of medication. However, if a schizophrenic patient does not respond to antipsychotic drugs, it is generally not a good idea to increase them. Why not?

Increased doses increase the risk of tardive dyskinesia.

4. Long-term use of antipsychotic drugs can induce tardive dyskinesia. However, if a person with tardive dyskinesia stops taking the drugs, the symptoms actually grow worse, at least temporarily. Why?

The symptoms are probably due, at least in large part, to denervation supersensitivity. After prolonged blockage of dopamine synapses, the synapses become more sensitive to even the small amount of dopamine that reaches them. If someone stops taking antipsychotic drugs at that time, more dopamine reaches the synapses, which are already oversensitive.

5. Why might it sometimes be difficult to find effective drugs for someone who suffers from both depression and schizophrenia?

Antidepressant drugs increase activity at serotonin and catecholamine synapses. Antipsychotic drugs block activity at certain kinds of catecholamine synapses. The antipsychotic drug clozapine blocks serotonin type $5HT_2$ receptors.

Substance Abuse Questionnaire

A. Do not write your name on the questionnaire (responses are anonymous)
B. Please circle the most correct response
C. State both medical and recreational experiences

Age: _____   Sex: M   F

1. Do you smoke cigarettes (tobacco)?   No   Yes
2. Do you smoke other tobacco products (cigar, pipe, clove)? No   Yes
3. Do you chew or snuff tobacco?   No   Yes
4. Have you ever consumed marijuana or hashish?   No   Yes
5. Have you consumed marijuana/hashish within the last 30 days? No   Yes
6. Have you ever tried amphetamines (speed, crystal)?   No   Yes
7. Have you consumed amphetamines within the last 30 days?   No   Yes
8. Have you ever tried cocaine?   No   Yes
9. Have you ever tried crack cocaine (smoke freebase)?   No   Yes
10. Have you consumed cocaine within the last 30 days?   No   Yes
11. Have you ever tried:

        LSD (acid)?   No   Yes
        Heroin?   No   Yes
        Morphine?   No   Yes
        Barbiturates (e.g., Luminal, Nembutal, etc.)   No   Yes
        PCP (angel dust)?   No   Yes
        Darvon (propoxyphene)?   No   Yes
        Hallucinogenic mushrooms?   No   Yes
        Ecstasy (MDMA)?   No   Yes
        Inhalants (e.g., nitrous oxide, etc.)   No   Yes

12. Do you drink:

        alcoholic beverages?   No   Yes
        Some beer each week?   No   Yes
        Some wine each week?   No   Yes
        Some mixed drinks each week?   No   Yes

13. Within the last 30 days have you used:

        Prescription sleeping pills?   No   Yes
        Over-the-counter pain relievers?   No   Yes
        Minor tranquilizers (e.g., Xanax, etc.)?   No   Yes
        Diet pills?   No   Yes

14. Do you think you have a problem with substance abuse?   No   Yes

    If yes, which substance(s)_____